A LEVEL

Questions and Answers

STATISTICS

Clive Morris

Principal Examiner

SERIES EDITOR: BOB McDUELL

Letts
EDUCATIONAL

Contents

HOW TO USE THIS BOOK

The aim of the *Questions and Answers* series is to provide students with the help required to attain the highest level of achievement in important examinations. This book is intended to help you with the Statistics component of A- and AS-level Mathematics. The series relies on the idea that an experienced examiner can provide, through examination questions, sample answers and advice, the help students need to secure success. Many revision aids concentrate on providing factual information that might have to be recalled in an examination. This series, while giving factual information in an easy-to-remember form, concentrates on the other skills that need to be developed for the new A-level examinations which started in 1996.

The *Questions and Answers* series is designed to provide:

● Easy-to-use **Revision Summaries** that identify important factual information that students must understand if progress is to be made in answering examination questions.

● Advice on the different types of question in each subject and how to answer them well to obtain the highest marks.

● Information about other skills, apart from the recall of knowledge, that will be tested on examination papers. These are sometimes called **assessment objectives** and modern A-level examinations put great emphasis on them. The *Questions and Answers* series is intended to develop these skills, particularly those of communication, problem-solving, evaluation and interpretation, by the use of questions and the appreciation of outcomes by the student.

● Many examples of **examination questions**. Students can increase their achievement by studying a sufficiently wide range of questions, provided that they are shown the way to improve their answers to these questions. It is advisable that students try the questions first before looking at the answers and the advice that accompanies them. All the questions come from actual examination papers or specimen materials issued by the British Examination Boards, reflecting their requirements.

● **Sample answers** and mark schemes to all the questions.

● **Advice from examiners**: by using the experience of actual examiners we are able to give advice that can enable students to see how their answers can be improved to ensure greater success.

Success in A-level examinations comes from proper preparation and a positive attitude, developed through a sound knowledge of facts and an understanding of principles. These books are intended to overcome 'examination nerves' which often come from a fear of not feeling properly prepared.

THE IMPORTANCE OF USING QUESTIONS FOR REVISION

Past examination questions play an important part in revising for examinations. However, it is important not to start practising questions too early. Nothing can be more disheartening than trying to do a question that you do not understand because you have not mastered the concepts. Therefore it is important to have studied a topic thoroughly before attempting questions on it.

It is unlikely that any question you try will appear in exactly the same form on the papers you are going to take. However the number of totally original types of question that can be set on any part of the syllabus is limited and so similar ideas occur over and over again. It certainly will help you if the question you are trying to answer in an examination is familiar and you are used to the type of language used. Your confidence will be boosted, and confidence is important for examination success.

Practising examination questions will also highlight gaps in your knowledge and understanding so that you can go back and revise more thoroughly. It will indicate which sorts of question you can do well and which, if there is a choice, you should avoid.

Finally, having access to answers, as you do in this book, will enable you to see clearly what is required by the examiner, how best to answer each question and the amount of detail required. Remember that attention to detail is a very important aspect of achieving success at A-level.

MAXIMISING YOUR MARKS IN STATISTICS

One of the keys to examination success is to know how marks are gained or lost and the examiner's tips given with the solutions in this book give hints on how you can maximise your marks on particular questions. However you should also take careful note of these general points:

● Check the requirements of your examination board and follow carefully the instructions (or 'rubric') about the number of questions to be tackled. Many examinations in A-level Mathematics subjects instruct you to attempt all the questions and where papers start with short, straightforward questions, you are advised to work through them in order so that you build up your confidence. Do not overlook any parts of a question – double-check that you have seen everything, including any questions on the back page! If there is a choice, do the correct number. If you do more, you will not be given credit for any extra and it is likely that you will not have spent the correct time on each question and that your answers may suffer as a result. Take time to read through all the questions carefully, and then start with the question you think you can do best.

● Get into the habit of setting out your work neatly and logically. If you are untidy and disorganised you could penalise yourself by misreading your own figures or lose marks because your method is not obvious. Always show all necessary working so that you can obtain marks for a correct method even if your final answer is wrong. Remember that a good clear sketch can help you to see important details of how to tackle a question.

● When the question asks for a particular result to be established, remember that to obtain the method marks you must show sufficient working to convince the examiner that your argument is valid. Do not rely too heavily on your graphical calculator.

● Do not be sloppy with algebraic notation or manipulation, especially when using brackets and negatives. Do rough estimates of calculations to make sure that they are reasonable, state units if applicable and give answers to the required degree of accuracy; do not approximate prematurely in your working.

● Make sure that you interpret your answers in the context of the questions and be careful that your answers make sense in that context.

● Make sure that you are familiar with the formulas booklet and tables that you will be given in the examination and learn any useful formulas that are not included. Refer to the booklet in the examination and transfer details accurately.

● When about 15 minutes remain, check whether you are running short of time. If so, try to score as many marks as possible in the short time that remains, concentrating on the easier parts of any questions not yet tackled.

● The following glossary may help you in answering questions:
  Write down, state – no justification is needed for an answer.
  Calculate, find, determine, show, solve – include enough working to make your method clear.
  Deduce, hence – make use of the given statement to establish the required result.
  Sketch – show the general shape of a graph, its relationship with the axes, any asymptotes and points of special significance such as turning points.
  Draw – plot accurately, using graph paper and selecting a suitable scale; this is usually preparation for reading information from the graph.
  Find the <u>exact</u> value – leave it in fractions or surds, or in terms of logarithms, exponentials or π; note that using a calculator is likely to introduce decimal approximations, resulting in loss of marks.

Data collection and sampling 1

All statistical work relies on the collection, organisation, presentation, analysis and interpretation of **data**. Data can be **primary data** (collected and used for a particular purpose) or **secondary data** (used for a different purpose to the one for which it was originally collected).

Data may be of two types. **Qualitative data** is that which can be **categorised**, for example hair colour, make of car, etc. **Quantitative data** is numerical data which can be **counted** or **measured**, for example number of brothers, height, etc. Quantitative data can be **discrete** (it can only take certain fixed values, for example it is only possible to have 0, 1, 2, 3,…brothers) or **continuous** (it can take any value within a given range, for example heights). Note that continuous measurements can sometimes appear discrete, for example heights might be measured to the nearest centimetre. It is important to recognise the difference since different forms of graphical presentation are used for discrete and continuous data.

Data is usually collected by using **questionnaires** or by **direct observation**. Care needs to be taken when designing questionnaires to ensure that they can be answered easily and that they provide accurate and relevant data in a form which can be processed easily. Attention needs to be given to layout, working and logical design as well as to the best way for the questionnaire to be completed.

When undertaking statistical research the whole group of people or objects in which we are interested is known as the **population**; each member of the population is called a **unit**. Due to factors such as time, practicality or destructiveness of a product it is not usually possible to gain information about the whole population. Instead, information about a subgroup of the population called a **sample** is obtained. A sample can be chosen by selecting units from a **sampling frame** (a suitable list of some sort, for example a telephone directory or electoral register) which may or may not contain the whole population. The sampling process needs to be designed in such a way as to avoid **bias** (obtaining a false picture of the truth) and to ensure **precision** (so that repeated samples would produce similar results with as little variation as possible).

Types of sampling process include:

● **Random sampling** where each member of the population has an equal chance of being selected. A simple random sample is one in which units are taken without replacement.

● **Stratified sampling** where the sample is made of the same proportions from within different groupings (strata) as the population.

● **Purposive (systematic) sampling** where every nth unit is chosen.

● **Quota sampling** where certain numbers of units in certain categories are required.

● **Cluster sampling** where the units in naturally-occurring groupings (clusters) are examined.

● **Multi-stage sampling** which involves combinations of the other types. For example, an interviewer might select certain countries at random, then certain cities within each country at random, then certain roads using a stratified approach, and then use purposive sampling to obtain a sample.

If you need to revise this subject more thoroughly, see the relevant topics in the *Letts* **A level** *Mathematics* *Study Guide.*

When a sample has been obtained, appropriate **sample statistics** are calculated and used to **estimate population parameters.** For example, the **sample mean,** $\bar{x}$ can be used as an estimate for the **population mean,** μ.

1 The *Guardian* newspaper commissioned the market research firm ICM to conduct an opinion poll, publishing the results on 17th February 1995 with the following explanation.

ICM interviewed a quota sample of 1427 adults, aged 18-plus, in 103 randomly selected parliamentary constituencies country-wide.

(a) Describe a suitable random process for selecting 103 constituencies, clearly identifying the sampling frame you would use. There are 651 parliamentary constituencies. (3)

(b) Making reference to the above quotation, explain the meaning of a *quota sample.* (2)

NEAB

2 Two researchers investigated the hours worked by retail managers. A trade gazette lists 12 000 retail managers, numbering them from 1 to 12 000. Each researcher undertook to obtain information from a random sample.

(a) One researcher, John, chose to use the random decimal generator on his calculator. The first random decimals produced on the calculator were:

$$0.162, 0.991, 0.524.$$

John decided to multiply each by 10 000 and select the manager corresponding to this number.

(i) Which are the first two managers selected by John's method? (1)

(ii) State one feature which John's method shares with that of obtaining a random sample. (1)

(iii) Criticise two features of his method. (2)

(b) Another researcher, Jane, used the six digit random decimal generator on a computer. The first three random decimals it produced were:

$$0.071\,656, \quad 0.643\,815, \quad 0.198\,408.$$

Jane decided to multiply each by 12 000 and, ignoring the decimal part of the product, select the corresponding manager.

(i) State the number of the first manager selected by Jane's method. (1)

(ii) State why Jane's method is an improvement over John's. (1)

(iii) State one criticism of Jane's method. (1)

UODLE

3 On a particular day there are 2125 books on the shelves in the **fiction** section of a library.

(a) Describe how random numbers could be used to select a random sample of size 20 (without replacement) from the 2125 books. (4)

The number of times each book in the sample has been borrowed in the last year is found by counting the appropriate date stamps inside the front cover. The sample mean is used as an estimate of the mean for all books belonging to the **fiction** section of the library.

(b) How is the estimate likely to be affected by the fact that:

(i) some books will not be on the shelves due to being in the possession of borrowers;

(ii) new books will have been on the shelves for less than a year? (4)

(c) Give a reason, other than those mentioned in (b), why the sample will not be representative of **all** the books in the library. (1)

(d) Discuss, briefly, how the problems, identified in (b) and (c), of estimating the mean number of times per year books in the library are borrowed could be overcome. (4)

AEB

Data in the form in which it has been collected is called **raw data** and when deciding suitable ways of collecting data thought should be given to how the data can best be arranged in a helpful, logical way so that they can be assimilated and interpreted easily. Tabulation is often helpful and this can be organised using **tallies**. Where necessary, such as in the case of continuous or discrete data which takes a large number of possible values, the data can be put into **groups** or **classes**.

A **bar chart** or **line diagram** can be used to represent qualitative or discrete quantitative data. The height of the bar or line represents the frequency. A **pie chart** can be used in similar circumstances: the areas of the pie slices represent the frequencies. For example, a pie chart representing twice the total frequency of another pie chart should have a total area twice as large. Its radius should therefore be $\sqrt{2}$ times the radius of the smaller pie chart.

A **stem and leaf diagram** can be used to represent discrete quantitative data so that the original data is still visible as shown in this example.

Number of years experience of 38 teaching staff at a school

Women								Men					
		8	5	1	1	0	1	1	4	5	7	9	
7	5	4	3	1	1	1	0	1	2	2	9		
	5	4	4	1	1	2	2	3	4	6	6	7	
				4	2	3	1	4	4	5			

A **histogram** can be used to represent grouped discrete or continuous data. This differs from a bar chart in that:

- There is a scale on the axis representing the variable.
- The bars can touch each other as adjacent classes have a common boundary.
- The areas of the bars represent frequencies.
- The vertical scale is **frequency density** *not* frequency.

Frequency density = height of bar = $\dfrac{\text{frequency}}{\text{class width}}$

Note that the bars begin and end at **class boundaries**.

A **frequency polygon** or (for a large set of data with a large number of classes) a **frequency curve** can be obtained by joining the **mid-points** of the tops of the bars with straight lines or a curve respectively.

Grouped discrete or continuous data can also be represented by a **cumulative frequency polygon** or **cumulative frequency curve** depending on whether straight lines or a curve are used. Cumulative frequencies are usually calculated on a *less than* basis using **upper class boundaries** and cumulative frequencies are then plotted against the upper class boundaries.

Be aware that you may be asked to give the advantages and disadvantages of different types of graphical presentation.

As well as being presented graphically, data can also be summarised numerically. The three most common **measures of location** or **averages** are the mean, median and mode.

The **mean** uses every data value and is given for frequency distributions by $\bar{x} = \dfrac{\sum fx}{\sum f}$.

You can probably use the statistical functions on your calculator to find the mean if you are given the data itself but you need to know how to use the formulas as you may be given summary information instead. For grouped data you should use the mid-class values as your *x*-values. This also applies later to calculating the variance and standard deviation.

REVISION SUMMARY

The **median** Q_2 is the middle value when the data is written in order of size. For n items the median is the $\frac{n+1}{2}$th item. For grouped data the median can be found by reading off a cumulative frequency curve or by using **linear interpolation**. The median is preferred to the mean when the distribution is **skewed** or when there are **outliers**.

The **mode** is the value that occurs most frequently. If the data has been grouped then the **modal class** is the one with the largest frequency density.

Measures of dispersion or **spread** indicate how much variation there is within the data. The most basic of these is the **range** which is the difference between the largest and smallest data values. The range is affected badly by extreme values.

The **standard deviation** (which is the square root of the **variance**) uses every value in the data.

For a sample, the standard deviation is $s = \sqrt{\dfrac{\sum f(x - \bar{x})^2}{\sum f}}$.

This can be shown to be equal to $s = \sqrt{\dfrac{\sum fx^2}{\sum f} - \bar{x}^2}$ which is easier to calculate. Watch out in this area of the syllabus for slight differences in terminology and notation between different examination boards. As with the mean, you can probably use the statistical functions on your calculator to work out the standard deviation and variance when the data is given. Make sure you can also use the formulas when you are just given the relevant summary statistics.

In most distributions the vast majority of the data lies within three standard deviations of the mean.

You should also be aware of the use of **coding** in calculations of the mean and standard deviation. When the data is skewed a better measure of spread is the **interquartile range**. This is the numerical difference between the **upper quartile**, Q_3 (the $\frac{3}{4}(n+1)$th value) and the **lower quartile**, Q_1 (the $\frac{1}{4}(n+1)$th value).

A **box and whisker plot** can be used to represent the extremes of the data, the median and the quartiles. The **skewness** of the distribution can thus be assessed. If $Q_3 - Q_2 > Q_2 - Q_1$, the distribution has positive (or right) skew. If $Q_3 - Q_2 < Q_2 - Q_1$, the distribution has negative (or left) skew.

As well as these absolute measures of dispersion there are relative measures of dispersion such as $\dfrac{\text{standard deviation}}{\text{mean}}$ or $\dfrac{\text{interquartile range}}{\text{median}}$ which compare the relative sizes of a measure of dispersion and the corresponding measure of location.

If you need to revise this subject more thoroughly, see the relevant topics in the *Letts* A level Mathematics Study Guide.

We will return in Unit 8 to talk in greater detail about **statistical estimates** but it is worth mentioning a couple now. A **statistical estimator** is a **sample statistic** which is calculated in order to estimate a **population parameter**. These estimates should be **unbiased** (that is they should produce on average a correct value for the appropriate population parameter) and should have the **smallest variance** possible.

An unbiased estimate for the population mean μ is provided by the sample mean $\bar{x}$ and an unbiased estimate for the population variance σ^2 is provided by $\hat{\sigma}^2 = \dfrac{(\sum f)s^2}{\sum f - 1}$.

This can be written as $\hat{\sigma}^2 = \dfrac{1}{\sum f - 1}\left(\sum fx^2 - \dfrac{(\sum fx)^2}{\sum f}\right)$.

Different examination boards use slightly different notations so make sure that you are familiar with the one that your examination board uses.

1   In ten pin bowling the player attempts to knock down all 10 skittles with one ball. If all 10 are knocked down the player's turn ends without a second ball being bowled, but if any skittles are left standing the player attempts to knock them down with a second ball. After the second ball the players turn ends even if some skittles remain standing. A novice player bowls a total of 34 balls. The numbers of skittles knocked down per ball are as follows.

Number of skittles	0	1	2	3	4	5	6	7	8	9	10
Frequency	6	3	1	7	8	3	2	3	0	1	0

(i)   Use your calculator to determine the mean and standard deviation of the numbers of skittles knocked down per ball.   (4)

The diagrams below show, for two players *A* and *B*, the numbers of skittles knocked down per ball. (No scale is given on the frequency axis, but the data are for many hundreds of balls bowled.)

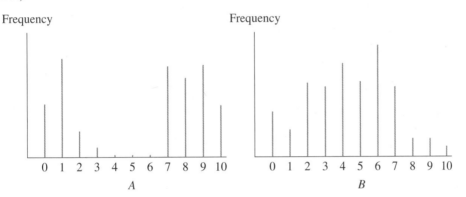

(ii)   Without performing any calculations, **estimate** the mean number of skittles per ball knocked down by each of players *A* and *B*.   (3)

(iii)   Without performing any calculations, compare the standard deviations for the two sets of data, explaining your reasoning.   (3)

(iv)   One of the players is a considerably better bowler than the other. State which is which, giving your reasons carefully.   (4)

Oxford & Cambridge (MEI)

2   The table gives the ages, in completed years, of the population in a particular region of the United Kingdom.

Age	0–4	5–15	16–44	45–64	65–79	80 and over
Number (in thousands)	260	543	1727	756	577	135

A histogram of this data was drawn with age along the horizontal axis. The 0–4 age group was represented by a bar of horizontal width 0.5 cm and height 5.2 cm.

(a)   Find the widths and heights, in cm to 1 decimal place, of the bars representing the following age groups:

(i) 16–44,   (ii) 65–79.

(b)   Taking the mid-point of the last group to be 90 years write down the mid-points of the other age groups and estimate the mean age of the population in this region of the United Kingdom.   (11)

London Examinations

3 In the casualty reception area of a hospital, the time, t hours, between the arrival of patients with broken limbs is recorded. The table shows the cumulative frequency for the first 100 times recorded.

Time (t)	< 0.25	< 0.5	< 1.0	< 2.0	< 4.0	< 12.0	< 24.0
Cumulative frequency	20	38	62	86	98	99	100

(a) Write down the cumulative frequency of the median time. (1)

(b) Use linear interpolation to estimate the median time. (4)

(c) Estimate the proportion of times which exceed 3 hours. (2)

UODLE

4

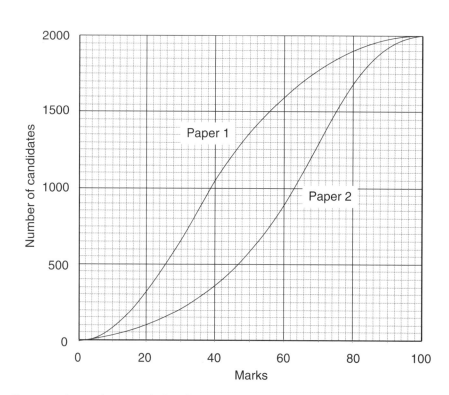

The diagram shows the cumulative frequency graphs for the marks scored by the candidates in an examination. The 2000 candidates each took two papers; the upper curve shows the distribution of marks on paper 1 and the lower curve shows the distribution on paper 2. The maximum mark on each paper was 100.

(i) Draw an accurate diagram representing these marks by means of a pair of box and whisker plots. (5)

(ii) Give three brief comments on any advantages or disadvantages in these methods of representing the data. (3)

UCLES

5 In an investigation children were asked a number of questions about their journeys to school. The data collected are to be illustrated using pie charts, line diagrams or histograms. (In answering this question you should only consider these three types of diagram.)

Question 1 asked the children whether they had travelled to school by bicycle, bus, train, car or on foot.

(a) Which type of diagram would best illustrate the proportion of children using each method of transport? (1)

Question 2 asked the children on how many of the last 5 days they had travelled to school by car. A summary of the results is shown below.

Number of days by car	0	1	2	3	4	5
Number of children	112	32	18	7	29	64

(b) Illustrate these data using a suitable diagram. Comment briefly on the shape of the distribution. (4)

Question 3 asked the children how long their journeys to school had taken on a particular day. A summary of the results is shown below.

Time (minutes)	0.5–15.5	15.5–25.5	25.5–35.5	35.5–55.5	55.5–90.5
Number of children	129	52	34	26	21

(c) Illustrate these data using an appropriate diagram. (7)

AEB

6   Summarised below is the data relating to the number of minutes, to the nearest minute, that a random sample of 65 trains from Darlingborough were late arriving at a main line station.

	Minutes late (0 $\vert$ 2 means 2)	Totals
0	2 3 3 3 4 4 4 4 5 5 5 5 5 5	(14)
0	6 6 6 7 7 8 8 8 9	(9)
1	0 0 0 2 2 3 3 4 4 4 5	( )
1	6 6 7 7 8 8 8 9 9	( )
2	1 2 2 3 3 3 3 4	( )
2	6	( )
3	3 4 4 5	(4)
3	6 8	(2)
4	1 3	(2)
4	7 7 9	(3)
5	2 4	(2)

(a) Write down the values needed to complete the stem and leaf diagram.

(b) Find the median and the quartiles of these times.

(c) Find the 67th percentile.

(d) On graph paper construct a box plot for these data, showing clearly your scale.

(e) Comment on the skewness of the distribution.

A random sample of trains arriving at the same main line station from Shefton had a minimum value of 15 minutes late and a maximum value of 30 minutes. The quartiles were 18, 22 and 27 minutes.

(f) On the same graph paper and using the same scale, construct a box plot for these data.

(g) Compare and contrast the train journeys from Darlingborough and Shefton based on these data. (20)

London Examinations

3 *Probability*

Probabilities measure how likely something is to happen. They always have values between 0 (representing something which is impossible) and 1 (representing something which is certain to happen) inclusive. Remembering this fundamental point can save you many marks!

The set of all possible outcomes for an experiment is called the **sample space**. A number of possible outcomes considered together is called an **event**. If each outcome in a sample space is equally likely (has the same chance of occurring) then the probability of an event A happening is given by $P(A) = \dfrac{r}{n}$ where r is the total number of outcomes which result in A happening and n is the total number of possible outcomes.

Venn diagrams can be very helpful to illustrate problems and to help solve them. As a reminder of notation:

$\overline{A}$ or A' means A does not happen (the complement of A).

$A \cup B$ means A or B (or both) happen.

$A \cap B$ means both A and B happen.

The **addition law of probability** states that $P(A \cup B) = P(A) + P(B) - P(A \cap B)$.

Two events A and B are said to be **mutually exclusive** if and only if $P(A \cap B) = 0$ that is if both A and B cannot both happen. In this case the addition law reduces to $P(A \cup B) = P(A) + P(B)$.

If the event A has happened then the **conditional probability** of B happening given that A has happened is $P(B \mid A) = \dfrac{P(B \cap A)}{P(A)}$. This can be rewritten as $P(B \cap A) = P(A)\, P(B \mid A)$.

Two events A and B are said to be **independent** if and only if the occurrence (or non-occurrence) of one does not affect the occurrence (or non-occurrence) of the other. A condition for two events A and B to be independent is that $P(B \mid A) = P(B)$. Conversely if $P(B \mid A) = P(B)$ then A and B are independent. An equivalent condition is that $P(A \cap B) = P(A)\, P(B)$ if and only if A and B are independent.

Two events are said to be **exhaustive** if and only if $P(A \cup B) = 1$. Two events are said to be **complementary** if and only if they are both exhaustive and mutually exclusive. If two events A and B are complementary then $P(A) + P(B) = 1$ or $P(B) = 1 - P(A)$. Note that A and $\overline{A}$ are complementary events.

The **reversal law** which is derived from the result for conditional probability is that

$$P(B \mid A) = \frac{P(A \mid B)\, P(B)}{P(A)}.$$

When this is combined with the **law of total probability**

i.e. $P(A) = P(A \cap B) + P(A \cap \overline{B}) = P(A \mid B)P(B) + P(A \mid \overline{B})P(\overline{B})$

we obtain **Bayes' Theorem** which states that

$$P(B \mid A) = \frac{P(A \mid B)P(B)}{P(A \mid B)P(B) + P(A \mid \overline{B})P(\overline{B})}$$

These results can be extended for three (or more) events to give the following results for three events A, B and C:

- $P(A \cup B \cup C) = P(A) + P(B) + P(C) - P(A \cap B) - P(A \cap C) - P(B \cap C) + P(A \cap B \cap C)$

- If A, B and C are also pairwise mutually exclusive (that is, no two can happen at the same time) then

$P(A \cup B \cup C) = P(A) + P(B) + P(C).$

$P(A \cap B \cap C) = P(A)\, P(B\,|\,A)\, P(C\,|\,B \cap A)$

- If A, B and C are also independent then

$P(A \cap B \cap C) = P(A)\, P(B)\, P(C)$

- If $A_1, A_2 \ldots, A_n$ are pairwise mutually exclusive (that is, no two can happen at the same time) and exhaustive then

$P(A_1 \cup A_2 \cup \ldots \cup A_n) = P(A_1) + P(A_2) + \ldots + P(A_n) = 1$

Tree diagrams can be extremely valuable in solving probability problems. The probability of events which happen together are obtained by multiplying probabilities along consecutive branches of the tree. Either/or probabilities are obtained by adding probabilities at the end of the branches of the tree.

Possibility space diagrams can also be helpful particularly when dealing with problems which require assigning probabilities to a function of two variables such as the sum of the scores on two fair dice.

Permutations and **combinations** are used when the number of **arrangements** (order is important) or **selections** (order is not important) of a number of objects or people needs to be determined. Some useful results are:

- The number of arrangements of n different objects in a straight line is $n!$

- The number of arrangements of n objects where s are the same and the rest are all different is

$\dfrac{n!}{s!}$

- The number of arrangements of n different objects taken r at a time is ${}^nP_r = \dfrac{n!}{(n-r)!}$

- The number of arrangements of n different objects in a circle is $(n-1)!$

or $\dfrac{(n-1)!}{2}$ if clockwise and anticlockwise arrangements are taken to be the same.

- The number of selections of n different objects taken r at a time (when the order of selection is unimportant) is $\dbinom{n}{r} = \dfrac{n!}{(n-r)!\,r!}$. (Sometimes the notation ${}^nC_r$ is used for this.)

- The number of selections that can be made from n different objects (excluding a selection of nothing) is $2^n - 1$.

If you need to revise this subject more thoroughly, see the relevant topics in the *Letts* A level Mathematics Study Guide.

When tackling probability questions try not to become too obsessed with formulas but think clearly about what is happening in the given problem and then choose the formulas which are relevant in the situation.

1   I sit in a cafe and watch people go by. For each person that goes by, the probability that I know their name is 0.04. Assuming independence, find the probability that the fifth person who goes by is the first person whose name I know, giving your answer correct to 3 decimal places.   (2)
                                                                                                    UCLES

2   (i)   A fair coin is tossed until a head has been obtained. Find the probability that exactly 5 tosses are required.   (1)

    (ii) A fair coin is tossed until both a head and a tail have been obtained. Find the probability that exactly 5 tosses are required.   (2)
                                                                                                    UCLES

3   A diagnostic test is used to detect a certain disease which is known to afflict 3% of the population. When applied to a person with the disease, it gives a positive response with probability 0.95; when applied to a person who does not have the disease, it gives a positive response with probability 0.01. The test is applied to a randomly chosen member of the population.

    (a)   Calculate the probability that a positive response is obtained.   (3)

    (b)   Given that a positive response is obtained, calculate the probability that the person has the disease.   (2)
                                                                                                    WJEC

4   The registration plate on my car is

    > K 364 WAM

    I am intending to buy a new car soon. Assuming that the new registration plate has three digits, and that all 900 sets of three digits from 100 to 999 are equally likely, calculate the probabilities of the following events.

    (i)   The digits on the new plate are 364 in that order.   (1)

    (ii)   The digits are 3, 6 and 4 but in any order.   (2)

    (iii) The new plate has none of the digits 3, 6, 4, on it.   (3)

    (iv)   The new plate matches the old in just the first digit – e.g. **3**52 but not **3**74.   (4)

    (v)   The new plate matches the old in exactly one digit – e.g. **3**52 or 4**7**4 but not **3**74. (4)
                                                                                      Oxford & Cambridge (MEI)

5   There are 60 students in the sixth form of a certain school. Mathematics is studied by 27 of them, biology by 20 and 22 students study neither mathematics nor biology.

    (a)   Find the probability that a randomly selected student studies both mathematics and biology.

    (b)   Find the probability that a randomly selected mathematics student does not study biology.

    A student is selected at random.

    (c)   Determine whether the event 'studying mathematics' is statistically independent of the event 'not studying biology'.   (10)
                                                                                      London Examinations

6 There are 8 competitors in the final of a 100 m race. The first 3 competitors to complete the course will all receive medals.

(a) Calculate the number of different possible groups of medal winners.

Two of the competitors represent the *Arrows* athletics club, the other six represent different clubs.

(b) Find the probability that the *Arrows* win at least one medal. (5)

London Examinations

7 (i) An examination paper has 5 questions on it and candidates must answer any 3 of them. In how many ways can a candidate choose which questions to answer? (Note that the order in which the questions are answered is not important.) (2)

For each of the following examination papers determine the number of ways a candidate may choose the required number of questions. Continue to ignore the order in which questions are attempted. **Show your working clearly**.

(ii) The paper has 2 sections, *A* and *B*. *A* has 6 questions from which candidates must answer any 4; *B* has 5 questions from which candidates must answer any 3. (3)

(iii) The paper has 5 questions and the candidate must answer at least 3 questions. (4)

(iv) The paper has 3 sections, *A*, *B* and *C*, each with 2 questions. Candidates must answer 4 questions in total, including at least 1 from each section. (5)

Oxford & Cambridge (MEI)

8 Vehicles approaching a crossroad must go in one of three directions – left, right or straight on. Observations by traffic engineers showed that of vehicles approaching from the north, 45% turn left, 20% turn right and 35% go straight on. Assuming that the driver of each vehicle chooses direction independently, what is the probability that of the next three vehicles approaching from the north

(a) (i) all go straight on;

(ii) all go in the same direction;

(iii) two turn left and one turns right;

(iv) all go in different directions;

(v) exactly two turn left? (10)

(b) Given that three consecutive vehicles all go in the same direction, what is the probability that they all turn left? (4)

AEB

9 In a tea shop 70% of customers order tea with milk, 20% tea with lemon, and 10% tea with neither. Of those taking tea with milk $\frac{3}{5}$ take sugar, of those taking tea with lemon $\frac{1}{4}$ take sugar, and of those taking tea with neither milk nor lemon $\frac{11}{20}$ take sugar. A customer is chosen at random.

(i) Represent the information given on a tree diagram and use it to find the probability that the customer takes sugar. (6)

(ii) Find the probability that the customer takes milk or sugar or both. (3)

(iii) Find the probability that the customer takes sugar **and** milk. Hence find the probability that the customer takes milk **given that** the customer takes sugar. (5)

Oxford & Cambridge (MEI)

4 *Discrete random variables*

**REVISION
SUMMARY**

Often in statistics we use **statistical models** to help us **understand** and **interpret** real-life situations. These models can then be used to make **predictions**. When choosing a suitable model we need to consider the nature of the variable (whether it is discrete or continuous) and any other conditions which are relevant. It may well be that after examining the model critically we will **refine** it further.

A **discrete random variable** X takes values in a set $x_1, x_2, x_3, \ldots$ where $x_1 < x_2 < x_3 < \ldots$ The probabilities associated with these define the **probability mass function** $P(X = x_i)$, an important property of which is that $\displaystyle\sum_x P(X = x) = 1$.

The **mean** or **expectation** or **expected value** of X is defined by $\mu = E(X) = \sum x\, P(X = x)$. Sometimes the expected value can be found using symmetry.

The **variance** σ^2 is defined by $\sigma^2 = \operatorname{Var}(X) = E(X - \mu)^2$ where $E(X - \mu)^2 = \sum (x - \mu)^2\, P(X = x)$.

It can however be shown that this reduces to $\operatorname{Var}(X) = E(X^2) - \mu^2$ where $E(X^2) = \sum x^2\, P(X = x)$.

The **standard deviation** σ is defined by $\sigma = \sqrt{\operatorname{Var}(X)}$

It should be noted that, if a is a constant, $E(a) = a$ and $\operatorname{Var}(a) = 0$.

The mean and variance of a **linear function of** X are given by $E(aX \pm b) = aE(X) \pm b$ and $\operatorname{Var}(aX \pm b) = a^2 \operatorname{Var}(X)$ where a and b are constants.

The mean and variance of **linear combinations of two random variables** X and Y are given by $E(aX \pm bY) = aE(X) \pm bE(Y)$ and $\operatorname{Var}(aX \pm bY) = a^2\,\operatorname{Var}(X) + b^2\,\operatorname{Var}(Y)$.

It should be noted that the variance result is only true if X and Y are **independent**.

The cumulative distribution function $F(x) = P(X \leq x)$ is given by $F(x) = \displaystyle\sum_{x_i \leq x} P(X = x_i)$.

From this, medians, quartiles etc. can be approximated or, in rare cases, calculated exactly.

The mode is the value x of X for which $P(X = x)$ is the largest.

The **Bernouilli distribution** takes values 0 and 1 with probabilities $q = 1 - p$ and p respectively. $E(X) = p$ and $\operatorname{Var}(X) = p(1 - p) = pq$.

The **Binomial distribution B(n, p)** is used to model the number of successes in an experiment with n independent trials where the probability of success in each trial, p, is constant.

$P(X = x) = \dbinom{n}{x} p^x q^{n-x}$ where $x = 0, 1, 2, \ldots, n$ and $q = 1 - p$

$E(X) = np$ and $\operatorname{Var}(X) = npq$.

A Binomial distribution can be thought of as the sum of n independent identically distributed Bernouilli distributions.

The **Binomial recurrence formula** can be used to speed up the calculation of successive Binomial probabilities. This is given by $P(X = x + 1) = \dfrac{(n - x)}{(x + 1)} \cdot \dfrac{p}{(1 - p)}\, P(X = x)$.

The **Geometric distribution Geo(p)** is used to model the number of trials in an experiment up to, and including the first success, where p is the constant probability of success in each trial.

$P(X = x) = q^{x-1} p$ where $x = 1, 2, 3, \ldots$ and $q = 1 - p$.

$E(X) = \dfrac{1}{p}$ and $\text{Var}(X) = \dfrac{q}{p^2}$.

The **Uniform distribution** is used to model situations in which each outcome is equally likely.

$P(X = x) = \dfrac{1}{n}$ $x = 1, 2, 3, \ldots, n$

$E(X) = \dfrac{n+1}{2}$ and $\text{Var}(X) = \dfrac{n^2 - 1}{12}$.

The **Poisson distribution Po(μ)** is used to model situations where events occur independently and at random in a certain interval with a mean number of occurrences μ.

$P(X = x) = \dfrac{e^{-\mu} \mu^x}{x!}$ $x = 0, 1, 2, \ldots$

$E(X) = \mu$ and $\text{Var}(X) = \mu$.

It should be noted that if two independent Poisson distributions with means μ_1 and μ_2 are added together then the result is another Poisson distribution with mean $\mu_1 + \mu_2$.

The **Poisson recurrence formula** can be used to speed up the calculation of successive Poisson probabilities. This is given by $P(X = x + 1) = \dfrac{\mu}{x+1} P(X = x)$

The Poisson distribution can be used as an **approximation to the Binomial distribution** using $X \sim \text{Po}(np)$ where n and p are the number of trials and the probability of success respectively in the Binomial distribution which is being approximated. The approximation can be used when n is large (say > 50) and p is small (say < 0.1). This ensures that $np \approx npq$, that is, the mean and variance are approximately equal.

It should be noted that the cumulative distribution functions for Binomial and Poisson variables are often tabulated for chosen values of n, p and μ. You should familiarise yourself with the relevant sections of your tables as using them often makes problems much quicker to solve. Useful identities when using these tables include

$P(a \le X \le b) = P(X \le b) - P(X \le (a - 1))$ and

$P(X \ge a) = 1 - P(X \le (a - 1))$.

The **Negative Binomial distribution** is used to model the number of trials up to and including the rth success. As before, trials are independent and the probability of success p in a particular trial is constant.

$P(X = x) = \dbinom{x-1}{r-1} p^x q^{x-r}$ where $x = r, r+1, r+2, \ldots$ and $q = 1 - p$

$E(X) = \dfrac{r}{p}$ and $\text{Var}(X) = \dfrac{rq}{p^2}$

If you need to revise this subject more thoroughly, see the relevant topics in the Letts A level Mathematics Study Guide.

4 *Discrete random variables*

QUESTIONS

1 A fair six-sided die is tossed four times. What is the probability that:

   (i) exactly one *six* occurs; (4)

   (ii) at least one *six* occurs. (5)

                                              NICCEA

2 The average number of calls put through to a telephone exchange during the half hour from 9.30 am to 10 am on weekdays is six. (You may assume that the Poisson model is adequate.)

   (i) Find the probability that, on a given weekday, between these times, the exchange will receive exactly four calls. (3)

   (ii) Find the probability that, on any given weekday, the exchange will receive more than three calls between 9.45 am and 10.00 am. (8)

                                              NICCEA

3 Breakdowns occur on a particular machine at a rate of 2.5 per month. Assuming that the number of breakdowns can be modelled by a Poisson distribution, find the probability that

   (a) exactly 3 occur in a particular month,

   (b) more than 10 occur in a 3 month period,

   (c) exactly 3 occur in each of 2 successive months. (6)

                                    London Examinations

4 A blue unbiased cubical die has one face marked 1, two faces marked 2 and three faces marked 3. A red unbiased cubical die has two faces marked 1, two faces marked 2 and two marked 3. The two dice are rolled together and X is the total score on the dice. Show that $P(X = 4) = \frac{1}{3}$, and draw up a table showing the probability distribution of X. (4)

Find the mean of X. (2)

                                              UCLES

5 Each packet of the breakfast cereal Fizz contains one plastic toy animal. There are five different animals. Each packet is equally likely to contain any of the five animals, independently of other packets. Without opening the packet it is impossible to tell which animal it contains. A family has already collected four different animals and at the start of a year they need to collect an elephant to complete their set. The family is interested in how many packets they will need to buy before they complete their collection.

   (i) Name an appropriate distribution with which to model this situation. (1)

   (ii) What is the probability that they will complete their collection with the third packet they buy after the start of the year? (2)

   (iii) Obtain the mean and variance of the number of packets needed, after the start of the year, to complete their collection. (3)

   (iv) What is the probability that, in order to complete their collection, they will need to buy more than 4 packets after the start of the year? (2)

                                              UCLES

6   The Weighton Cornershop Bakery produces fresh cream gateaux, making a profit of £3 on each one sold but losing £1 on each one unsold at the end of the day. Experience has shown that the daily demand for such gateaux can be modelled by a random variable X with a probability distribution as shown below.

x	0	1	2	3	4	5	6	7	8
$P(X = x)$	0.05	0.05	0.10	0.20	0.15	0.15	0.15	0.10	0.05

(a)   Show that the expected demand for gateaux on a given day is 4.2.   (2)

(b)   The random variable Y represents the daily profit when 8 gateaux are produced.

   (i)   Express Y in terms of X.   (1)

   (ii) Find the expected daily profit when 8 gateaux are produced.   (2)

(c)   The bakery is considering a reduction in the number of gateaux produced from 8 per day to 6 per day. Assuming the same model for demand, show that the expected daily profit is £10 when the bakery produces 6 gateaux per day.   (3)

(d)   Give a reason for

   (i)   supporting the change to 6 gateaux per day,   (1)

   (ii) not supporting the change to 6 gateaux per day.   (1)

NEAB

7   The owner of a hotel decides to sell copies of the local morning paper, the *Gazette*, to his guests. Assuming that he has n guests and that each guest, independently, wants to buy the *Gazette* with probability p, state the probability distribution that should be used to model the total number of guests wanting to buy the *Gazette*.   (1)

One morning, he has 20 guests and he decides to buy 4 copies of the *Gazette* for re-sale.

Assume that $p = 0.16$.

(a)   Calculate, correct to 4 decimal places, the probabilities that he sells 0, 1, 2, 3 copies of the *Gazette*.   (4)

(b)   **Deduce** the probability that he sells all 4 copies of the *Gazette*.   (2)

(c)   Each copy costs him 20p and sells for 50p; unsold copies have to be thrown away. Calculate, correct to the nearest penny, his expected profit from the sales of the *Gazette*.
(4)

WJEC

8 A model of a candidate's mark in an examination is as follows. The mark scored is modelled as $t + X$, where t is the mark which the candidate's true ability warrants and X is a random integer in the range –5 to 5. The distribution for X is taken to be

$$P(X = r) = P(X = -r) = k(6 - r) \quad r = 0, 1, 2, 3, 4, 5.$$

(i) Tabulate the distribution, show that $k = \frac{1}{36}$, and sketch the distribution. (4)

(ii) Write down the expectation of X and find the standard deviation of X. (3)

(iii) Find the probability of a candidate scoring a mark which is higher than his true ability warrants. (2)

Now suppose that candidates may take the examination on two or more occasions, with the highest mark being counted. Assume the candidate's true ability does not change.

(iv) Find the probability that the mark which counts is higher than the candidate's true ability warrants if he takes the examination

(A) twice,

(B) four times. (3)

(v) Explain, in the light of your answers to part (iv), what the model implies for candidates who take the examination repeatedly. Identify one weakness in the modelling assumptions. (2)

Oxford & Cambridge (MEI)

9 Ann and Brian are playing a game with two unbiased cubes. The red cube has one face marked with a 1, four faces with a 2 and one with a 3. The green cube has two faces marked with a 1, two with a 2 and two with a 3. Both cubes are rolled once and the independent random variables R and G represent the scores on the red cube and the green cube respectively.

(a) Find the probability distributions of R and G.

(b) Write down $E(R)$ and $E(G)$.

(c) Show that $\text{Var}(R) = \frac{1}{3}$ and find $\text{Var}(G)$.

Each player chooses two numbers α and β, $\alpha \geq 0$ and $\beta \geq 0$, in order to form a new random variable T where $T = \alpha R + \beta G$. Ann chooses $\alpha = 3$ and $\beta = 2$.

(d) Show that, for Ann, $E(T) = 10$ and find $\text{Var}(T)$.

Brian wishes to choose values for α and β so that $E(T) = 10$ but $\text{Var}(T)$ is as large as possible. He wonders whether to choose $\alpha = 5$, $\beta = 0$ or $\alpha = 0$, $\beta = 5$.

(e) Determine which of these he should choose and give a reason for your choice. (17)

London Examinations

Continuous random variables 5

A **continuous random variable** X takes values in a given range, $a \le x \le b$. X is defined by a probability density function f(x) which must be non-negative for all values of x in this range.

The probability of X being in a given range $c \le x \le d$ is given by the area under the curve $y = $ f(x)

between $x = c$ and $x = d$ which, using calculus, is given by $P(c \le X \le d) = \int_c^d f(x)\,dx$.

(Simple mensuration using areas of triangles, trapezia, etc can be very helpful in avoiding the use of calculus in certain cases.)

It should be noted that the total area under the curve $= \int_a^b f(x)\,dx = 1$.

The **mean** or **expectation** or **expected value** of X is given by $\mu = E(X) = \int_a^b x f(x)\,dx$. This can sometimes be found using symmetry.

The **variance** σ^2 is defined by $\sigma^2 = \text{Var}(X) = E(X^2) - \mu^2 = \int_a^b x^2 f(x)\,dx - \mu^2$.

The **standard deviation** σ is defined by $\sigma = \sqrt{\text{Var}(X)}$.
The expected value of a function g(X) can be found using $E(g(X)) = \int_a^b g(x) f(x)\,dx$.

The **cumulative distribution function** F(x) $= P(X \le x)$ is given by $F(x) = \int_a^x f(t)\,dt$. The **median** is therefore the value m for which $F(m) = 0.5$. The lower and upper quartiles Q_1 and Q_3 are those values of X for which $F(Q_1) = 0.25$ and $F(Q_3) = 0.75$ respectively.

If F(x) is known, then f(x) can be found using the relationship $f(x) = F'(x)$.

The **mode** is the value of X for which $f'(x) = 0$. This can be found using calculus.

If the probability density function of a random variable X is given by

$$f(x) = \begin{cases} \dfrac{1}{b-a} & a \le x \le b \\ 0 & \text{otherwise} \end{cases}$$

then X is said to have a **rectangular distribution** and we write $X \sim R(a, b)$.

$$E(X) = \frac{a+b}{2} \quad \text{and} \quad \text{Var}(X) = \frac{(b-a)^2}{12}. \qquad F(x) = \frac{x-a}{b-a}$$

If the probability density function of a random variable X is given by

$$f(x) = \begin{cases} \lambda e^{-\lambda x} & 0 \le x \le \infty \\ 0 & \text{otherwise} \end{cases}$$

where λ is a positive constant, X is said to have an **exponential distribution** with parameter λ.

$$E(X) = \frac{1}{\lambda} \quad \text{and} \quad \text{Var}(X) = \frac{1}{\lambda^2}. \qquad F(x) = 1 - e^{-\lambda x} \quad \text{and} \quad P(X > x) = e^{-\lambda x}.$$

The exponential distribution has the **loss of memory property**, that is, $P(X > a + b \mid X > a) = P(X > b)$. The exponential distribution can be used to model the waiting time between two successive occurrences of a Poisson distribution with mean λ.

If you need to revise this subject more thoroughly, see the relevant topics in the *Letts* A level Mathematics Study Guide.

19

1 Find the cumulative distribution function, F(x), for the random variable X which has the probability density function

$$f(x) = \begin{cases} \dfrac{1}{2} + \dfrac{1}{4}x & -2 \le x \le 0, \\[2mm] \dfrac{1}{2} - \dfrac{1}{4}x & 0 < x \le 2, \\[2mm] 0 & \text{elsewhere.} \end{cases}$$

(5)

UCLES

2 The lifetime, in thousands of hours, of a light-bulb is modelled by a continuous random variable X having probability density function

$$f(x) = \begin{cases} \dfrac{2}{5}x & 0 \le x \le 1, \\[2mm] \dfrac{1}{10}(5-x) & 1 < x < 5, \\[2mm] 0 & \text{otherwise.} \end{cases}$$

Using this model,

(i) find the probability that the lifetime of a randomly chosen light-bulb is less than 2000 hours, (3)

(ii) find the expected lifetime of a light-bulb. (3)

UCLES (adapted)

3 The student council of a college decide to organise a charity fun run in a local park. They want to design a course that all the runners will complete between 20 minutes and 80 minutes after the start of the run. They would also like the modal time taken by the runners to be about 40 minutes. The council devise a model for the time, T minutes, which a randomly chosen runner will take to complete the course. The probability density function, f, for T is defined below, where λ is a positive constant.

$$\begin{aligned} f(t) &= 2\lambda(t-20) & 20 \le t < 40, \\ f(t) &= \lambda(80-t) & 40 \le t \le 80, \\ f(t) &= 0 & \text{otherwise.} \end{aligned}$$

(a) Sketch the graph of the probability density function for $20 \le t \le 80$. (2)

(b) By considering your sketch, or otherwise, show that

$$\lambda = \tfrac{1}{1200}.$$ (3)

(c) The distribution function for T is F. By further consideration of your sketch, or otherwise, show that

(i) F(40) = $\tfrac{1}{3}$, (1)

(ii) F(t) = $1 - \tfrac{1}{2400}(80-t)^2$ for $40 \le t \le 80$. (3)

(d) The student council want to open a refreshment tent when about 60 per cent of the runners have finished the run. The run will start at 2.30 pm. Find the time that this model suggests for the tent to open. (4)

(e) Draw a sketch to illustrate a more realistic probability density function for T. Your sketch should still satisfy the conditions which the student council want to achieve. (1)

NEAB

4 A gardener is attempting to light a bonfire. The time, in minutes, for which a taper will stay alight on a calm day is modelled by the random variable T. The cumulative distribution function of T is given by

$$F(t) = P(T \leq t) = \begin{cases} 0 & t < 0, \\ \dfrac{1}{2}t^3 - \dfrac{3}{16}t^4 & 0 \leq t \leq 2, \\ 1 & t > 2. \end{cases}$$

(a) Find $P(T \leq 1)$.

(b) Verify that the median m of T satisfies $1.22 < m < 1.23$.

(c) Find the probability density function $f(t)$ of T.

(d) Find the modal time for which a taper will stay alight.

(e) Sketch the probability density function of T.

(f) Give a reason why this model may not be applicable on a windy day and give a sketch of a probability density function that may be more suitable in such conditions. (15)

London Examinations

5 The lifetime, in tens of hours, of a certain delicate electrical component is modelled by the random variable X with probability density function

$$f(x) = \begin{cases} k(9 - x), & 0 \leq x \leq 9, \\ 0, & \text{otherwise,} \end{cases}$$

where k is a positive constant.

(a) Show that $k = \frac{2}{81}$.

(b) Find the mean lifetime of a component.

(c) Show that the standard deviation of lifetimes is 21.2 hours.

(d) Find the probability that a component lasts at most 50 hours.

A particular device requires two of these components and it will not operate if one or more of the components fail. The device has just been fitted with two new components. The lifetimes of components are independent.

(e) Find the probability that the device will work for more than 50 hours.

(f) Give a reason why the above distribution may not be realistic as a model for the distribution of lifetimes of these electrical components. (17)

London Examinations

6 An analysis of historical data reveals that the time, in hours, between successive crashes of a computer network can be modelled by an exponential distribution with mean 90.

(a) Write down the probability that the time between two successive crashes is precisely 90 hours. (1)

(b) Find the probability that the time between two successive crashes is less than 180 hours. (2)

(c) Find the probability that the time between two successive crashes is more than 120 hours. (2)

NEAB

6 *The Normal distribution*

A continuous random variable X is said to follow a **Normal distribution** if the probability density function of X is

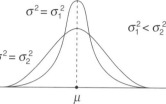

$$f(x) = \frac{1}{\sigma\sqrt{2\pi}} \exp\left\{\frac{-(x-\mu)^2}{2\sigma^2}\right\} \quad -\infty < x < \infty$$

where μ is the mean and σ^2 is the variance of X.

We write $X \sim N(\mu, \sigma^2)$. The Normal distribution is the most important continuous distribution. The shape of the curve $y = f(x)$ depends on μ and σ^2.

It should be noted that the curve is unimodal and symmetric.

If $X \sim N(\mu, \sigma^2)$ then the random variable Z, where $Z = \dfrac{X - \mu}{\sigma}$, is such that $Z \sim N(0, 1)$,

that is, it is Normal with mean 0 and variance 1. Tables can be used to find the cumulative distribution function of Z, $P(Z \leq z)$, and hence to find probabilities related to the distribution of X. Be aware however that you may come across three different types of tables.

Type I gives a shaded area which is $P(Z \leq z)$.

Type II gives a shaded area which is $P(0 \leq Z \leq z)$ that is, $P(Z \leq z) - 0.5$.

Type III gives a shaded area which is $P(Z > z)$, that is, $1 - P(Z \leq z)$

This book will assume the use of Type I tables which are the most common. Make sure that you are familiar with the ones used by your examining board.

Most tables give $P(Z \leq z)$ for z-values correct to 2 decimal places. $P(Z \leq z)$ for z-values given to more than 2 decimal places can be found using **linear interpolation**.

You should be familiar with the helpful relationships:

$P(Z > z) = 1 - P(Z \leq z)$ $\qquad\qquad$ $P(a \leq Z \leq b) = P(Z \leq b) - P(Z \leq a)$

$P(Z < -z) = 1 - P(Z \leq z)$ $\qquad\qquad$ $P(Z > -z) = P(Z \leq z)$

Also be aware that $P(Z \leq z) = P(Z < z)$ since Z is a continuous distribution.

For a Normal distribution

$P(\mu - \sigma \leq X \leq \mu + \sigma) = P(-1 \leq Z \leq 1) = 2P(Z \leq 1) - 1 = 0.6826$

$P(\mu - 2\sigma \leq X \leq \mu + 2\sigma) = P(-2 \leq Z \leq 2) = 2P(Z \leq 2) - 1 = 0.9544$

$P(\mu - 3\sigma \leq X \leq \mu + 3\sigma) = P(-3 \leq Z \leq 3) = 2P(Z \leq 3) - 1 = 0.9974$

Tables can be used to find z if $P(Z \leq z) = p$ where $0 \leq p \leq 1$ using **linear interpolation** where necessary.

Under certain conditions the Normal distribution can be used as an **approximation** to both the Poisson and Binomial distributions. A **continuity correction** must be used since a **continuous** distribution is being used to approximate a **discrete** distribution. Examples of continuity corrections are

$P(X \leq 4)$ becomes $P(X < 4.5)$ $P(X < 4)$ becomes $P(X < 3.5)$

$P(12 \leq X \leq 13)$ becomes $P(11.5 < X < 13.5)$

The conditions for using the approximations are given below:

Distribution	Normal distribution	Condition
$X \sim B(n, p)$	$X \sim N(np, npq)$	n large (> 30 say), $np > 5$, $nq > 5$
$X \sim Po(\mu)$	$X \sim N(\mu, \mu)$	μ large (> 20 say)

The approximation for the Binomial is better the nearer p is to 0.5 and the approximation for the Poisson gets better the larger μ is.

If $X_1, X_2, X_3, \ldots, X_n$ are independent Normal random variables with means $\mu_1, \mu_2, \mu_3, \ldots, \mu_n$ and variances $\sigma_1^2, \sigma_2^2, \sigma_3^2, \ldots, \sigma_n^2$ respectively then if $a_1, a_2, a_3, \ldots, a_n$ are constants,

$Y = a_1 X_1 + a_2 X_2 + a_3 X_3 + \ldots + a_n X_n$ is a Normal random variable with mean

$a_1 \mu_1 + a_2 \mu_2 + a_3 \mu_3 + \ldots + a_n \mu_n$ and variance $a_1 \sigma_1^2 + a_2 \sigma_2^2 + a_3 \sigma_3^2 + \ldots + a_n \sigma_n^2$.

In particular if $X_1, X_2, X_3, \ldots X_n$ are each $N(\mu, \sigma^2)$ then $X_1 + X_2 + X_3 + \ldots + X_n \sim N(n\mu, n\sigma^2)$.

In this case the **distribution of the sample mean** $\overline{X} = \dfrac{X_1 + X_2 + X_3 + \cdots + X_n}{n}$ is such that

$\overline{X} \sim N\left(\mu, \dfrac{\sigma^2}{n}\right)$.

The standard deviation of $\overline{X}$, $\dfrac{\sigma}{\sqrt{n}}$, is called the **standard error of the mean**.

It should be noted that if n is large (> 30 say) and if $X_1, X_2, X_3, \ldots, X_n$ are identically distributed with $E(X_i) = \mu$ and $Var(X_i) = \sigma^2$ then these two results are still approximately true even if

$X_1, X_2, X_3, \ldots, X_n$ are not Normally distributed.

That is, $X_1 + X_2 + X_3 + \ldots + X_n \sim N(n\mu, n\sigma^2)$ and $\overline{X} = \dfrac{X_1 + X_2 + X_3 \cdots + X_n}{n} \sim N\left(\mu, \dfrac{\sigma^2}{n}\right)$.

This set of results is known as the **Central Limit Theorem**.

If $X \sim B(n, p)$ and n is large (> 30 say) with $np > 5$ and $nq > 5$ then the **distribution of the**

sample proportion $P_s = \dfrac{X}{n}$ is approximately Normally distributed with mean p and variance $\dfrac{pq}{n}$

i.e. $P_s \sim N(p, \dfrac{pq}{n})$.

A continuity correction of $\pm \dfrac{1}{2n}$ as appropriate should be used.

6 The Normal distribution

1 (a) Give **two** reasons why the normal distribution is important in Statistics. (2)

   (b) An airline has a regular flight from one airport to another. The airline models the duration of a flight as a normally distributed random variable with a mean of 246 minutes and a standard deviation of 5 minutes. Use this model to calculate, to one decimal place, the percentage of these flights that are completed in less than 4 hours. (3)

   NEAB

2 An ordinary unbiased die is thrown 900 times. Using a suitable approximation, find the probability of obtaining at least 160 sixes. (5)

   UCLES

3 For **each** of the situations described below, name a distribution which might serve as a suitable model, stating values for the distribution's parameters. In **each** case, define fully a distribution which could be used as an approximation to your model.

   (a) The number of hay fever sufferers, in a random sample of 5000 sufferers, who are allergic to a certain drug, given that the probability that any sufferer is allergic to the drug is 0.0004. (3)

   (b) The number of minor faults in $50\,\text{m}^2$ of commercial carpet, given that minor faults occur independently at random in the carpet at a mean rate of 0.65 per m^2. (3)

   NEAB

4 An office block has a lift whose maximum permitted load is 500 kg. It is known that the weights of the men and the women using the lift can be modelled by normal distributions. The men's weights have mean 80 kg and standard deviation 12 kg. The women's weights have mean 56 kg and standard deviation 6 kg.

   On one occasion, 3 men and 4 women enter the lift. Calculate, correct to 2 significant figures, the probability that

   (a) their combined weight exceeds the maximum permitted load, (4)

   (b) the combined weight of the 3 men exceeds that of the 4 women. (4)

   WJEC

5 The number of letters received by a household on a weekday follows Poisson distribution with mean 2.8.

   (a) What is the probability that

      (i) on a particular weekday the household receives three or more letters; (2)

      (ii) the total number of letters received on ten successive weekdays is thirty or more? (You should use a suitable approximation.) (6)

   (b) Explain briefly why a Poisson distribution is unlikely to provide an adequate model for the number of letters received on a weekday throughout the year. (2)

   AEB

6 Electronic sensors of a certain type fail when they become too hot. The temperature at which a randomly chosen sensor fails is $T\,°\text{C}$, where T is modelled as a Normal random variable with mean μ and standard deviation σ.

   In a laboratory test, 98% of a random sample of sensors continued working at a temperature of 80°, but only 4% continued working at 104°.

   (i) Show the given information on a sketch of the distribution of T. (3)

   (ii) Determine estimates of the values of μ and σ. (4)

More extensive tests confirm that T is Normally distributed, but with $\mu = 94.5$ and $\sigma = 5.7$. Use these figures in the rest of the question.

(iii) Determine what proportion of sensors will operate in boiling water (i.e. at 100°C). (3)

(iv) The manufacturers wish to quote a safe operating temperature at which 99% of the sensors will work. What temperature should they quote? (4)

Oxford & Cambridge (MEI)

7   The continuous random variable X has probability density function

$$f(x) = \frac{3}{1024} \, x \, (x - 8)^2 \qquad 0 \le x \le 8.$$

A sketch of $f(x)$ is shown in the diagram.

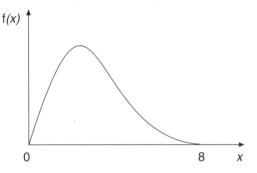

(i)   Find E(X) and show that Var(X) = 2.56. (5)

The times, in minutes, taken by a doctor to see her patients are modelled by the continuous random variable $T = X + 2$.

(ii) Sketch the distribution of T and describe in words what this model implies about the lengths of the doctor's appointments. (3)

(iii) Use the central limit theorem to find the probability that a set of 24 appointments will take less than 2 hours in total (i.e. less than 5 minutes each on average). You should assume that no time is lost through patients being late. (6)

Oxford & Cambridge (MEI)

8   Jam is packed into tins of advertised weight 1 kg. The weight of a randomly selected tin of jam is normally distributed about a target weight with a standard deviation of 12 g.

(a) If the target weight is 1 kg, find the probability that a randomly chosen tin weighs

   (i)   less than 985 g,

   (ii) between 970 g and 1015 g.

(b) If not more than one tin in 100 is to weigh less than the advertised weight, find the minimum target weight required to meet this condition.

(c) The target weight is fixed at 1 kg. The resulting tins are packed in boxes of 6 and the weight of the box is normally distributed with mean weight 250 g and standard deviation 10 g. Find the probability that a randomly chosen box of 6 tins will weigh less than 6.2 kg. (17)

London Examinations

7 *Bivariate data*

Bivariate data is data in which two variables are assigned to each member of a population, e.g. length and weight, shoe size and arm span, etc.

A **scatter diagram** can be used to represent bivariate data graphically.

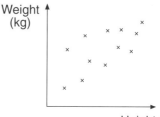

Linear correlation gives a measure of how well a straight line can be used to model a set of points on a scatter diagram. The correlation is **perfect** if the points lie exactly on a straight line. There are two commonly used **correlation coefficients** both giving values between -1 (perfect negative correlation) and $+1$ (perfect positive correlation) inclusive. The first is **Pearson's product-moment correlation coefficient**, r:

$$r = \frac{S_{xy}}{\sqrt{S_{xx}S_{yy}}} \quad \text{where} \qquad S_{xx} = \Sigma x^2 - \frac{(\Sigma x)^2}{n} \equiv \Sigma x^2 - n\bar{x}^2$$

$$S_{yy} = \Sigma y^2 - \frac{(\Sigma y)^2}{n} \equiv \Sigma y^2 - n\bar{y}^2$$

$$S_{xy} = \Sigma xy - \frac{(\Sigma x)(\Sigma y)}{n} \equiv \Sigma xy - n\bar{x}\,\bar{y}$$

and n is the number of pairs of data.

Pearson's product-moment correlation coefficient should only be used if the two variables are Normally distributed. Note that r is unaffected by coding the data.

The second correlation coefficient in use is **Spearman's rank correlation coefficient,** r_s where the data is ranked (equal values being given the average rank of those which would otherwise have been taken).

$$r_s = 1 - \frac{6\Sigma d^2}{n(n^2 - 1)} \quad \text{where } d \text{ is the difference in the ranks and } n \text{ is the number of pairs of data.}$$

This rank correlation coefficient can be used even when the data is not Normal.

Below are some examples of scatter diagrams and estimates of correlation coefficients.

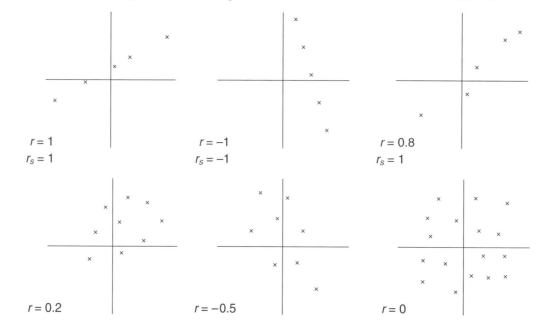

It should be noted that the existence of correlation between two variables does not imply cause and effect. It may be that the two variables are each related in turn to another variable which produces the change in both.

It is possible to have correlation which is not linear, for example quadratic correlation. You should know how to produce a linear correlation by using a new variable. In the example of quadratic correlation, if $y = ax^2 + b$ then y and h will be linearly correlated where $h = x^2$.

Tables can be used to carry out a hypothesis test to determine whether a calculated correlation coefficient suggests a linear relationship by being significantly different from zero. You will find further information on this in Unit 8.

If it appears that there is a linear relationship between two variables it is reasonable to find an equation which describes this relationship. In the case of linear correlation we are looking for a **regression line**. We can then use this to predict the value of one variable if we know the value of the other variable.

A **line of best fit** can be drawn by eye passing through $(\bar{x}, \bar{y})$ but a more refined approach is to obtain a **least squares** regression line by fixing the line in such a position that the sum of the squares of the **residuals** is minimised.

Except in the case of perfect correlation it is possible to identify two regression lines depending on whether the sum of the squares of the y-residuals is minimised (giving the regression line of y on x) or whether the sum of the squares of the x-residuals is minimised (giving the regression line of x on y).

Line	Equation	Used to predict
y on x	$y - \bar{y} = \dfrac{S_{xy}}{S_{xx}}(x - \bar{x})$ which is equivalent to $y = a + bx$ where $\quad b = \dfrac{S_{xy}}{S_{xx}}$ and $\quad a = \bar{y} - b\bar{x}$	a y-value given an x-value
x on y	$x - \bar{x} = \dfrac{S_{xy}}{S_{yy}}(y - \bar{y})$ which is equivalent to $x = c + dy$ where $\quad d = \dfrac{S_{xy}}{S_{yy}}$ and $\quad c = \bar{x} - d\bar{y}$	an x-value given a y-value

It may be that you can use your calculator to work out these regression lines using the raw data.

Note that both these regression lines pass through $(\bar{x}, \bar{y})$ and are identical if and only if $r = \pm 1$.

When using regression lines you should be aware of the dangers of **extrapolation**.

You must ensure that you know when to use correlation and when to use regression. Correlation is used to decide whether there is a relationship between two variables and to determine how strong such a relationship is. Regression is used to find a model for the relationship between two variables and to estimate values of one variable given values of the other variable.

If you need to revise this subject more thoroughly, see the relevant topics in the *Letts* A level *Mathematics Study Guide*.

1

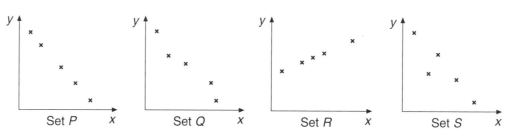

Set *P*   Set *Q*   Set *R*   Set *S*

The scatter diagrams illustrate four sets of bivariate data, *P*, *Q*, *R* and *S*.

(i)   State the value of the product-moment correlation coefficient for

  (a) data set *P*,   (1)

  (b) data set *R*.   (1)

(ii) Two of the data sets have the same value of Spearman's rank correlation coefficient.
    State which two sets they are.   (1)

UCLES

2   The number of hours *x* (correct to the nearest half-hour) spent studying for an examination
    by 12 students, together with the marks *y* achieved in the examination, are given in the
    following table.

x	2	3	4	$4\frac{1}{2}$	5	6	$6\frac{1}{2}$	8	$8\frac{1}{2}$	9	$9\frac{1}{2}$	10
y	44	50	60	54	65	73	81	89	84	90	103	120

$[\Sigma x = 76, \ \Sigma x^2 = 560, \ \Sigma y = 913, \ \Sigma y^2 = 75\ 153, \ \Sigma xy = 6425.]$

(i)   Calculate the product-moment correlation coefficient *r* for the data.   (3)

(ii) State what the value of *r* indicates about the relation between *x* and *y*.   (1)

(iii) The value of Spearman's rank correlation coefficient for the above data is 0.986, correct
    to 3 decimal places . For the next examination the students each increased their study
    time by 1 hour and there was an increase of 5 marks in each of their examination scores.
    Without further calculation, state whether the new value of the rank correlation
    coefficient, correct to 3 decimal places, is less than, equal to or greater than 0.986. Give
    a reason for your answer.   (2)

UCLES

3   A statistician discovers the following part of an old research paper.

> giving us mean values $\bar{x} = 21$ and $\bar{y} =$
> The line of regression of *y* on *x* may be written as $y = -\frac{1}{7}x +$
> and the line of regression of *x* on *y* may be written as $y = -7x + 163$.
> Treating *y* as the independent variable, we calculate that when *y* is
> known to be 128, an estimate for the value of *x* would be

(i)   Show that $\bar{y} = 16$.   (3)

(ii) Calculate the value of the missing term in the line of regression of *y* on *x*.   (2)

(iii) Use the appropriate line of regression to calculate the missing estimate for the value of x. (2)

(iv) Using a formula she knows, the statistician works out that the product-moment correlation coefficient r satisfies $r^2 = \frac{1}{49}$. Give a reason why the correct value of r is $-\frac{1}{7}$ and not $\frac{1}{7}$. (1)

(v) Use the value of the product-moment correlation coefficient to comment on the reliability of the estimated value of x. (2)

UCLES

4 The following data were collected during a study, under experimental conditions, of the effect of temperature, $x°C$, on the pH, y, of skimmed milk.

Temperature ($x°C$)	4	9	17	24	32	40	46	57	63	69	72	78
pH (y)	6.85	6.75	6.74	6.63	6.68	6.52	6.54	6.48	6.36	6.33	6.35	6.29

(a) Making reference to the following scatter diagram for these data, explain what it reveals about the relationship between x and y. (2)

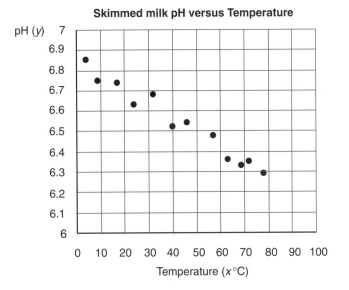

Skimmed milk pH versus Temperature

(b) Determine the equation of the least squares regression line of y on x. (5)

[You may make use of the following information.

$\sum x = 511$ $\sum y = 78.52$ $\sum x^2 = 28\ 949$ $\sum xy = 3291.88$]

(c) Interpret your values for the gradient and intercept of the regression line found in (b). (2)

(d) Estimate the pH of skimmed milk at $20°C$ and at $95°C$. In **each** case indicate, **with a reason but without further calculation**, how reliable you think these estimates might be. (4)

(e) Find the temperature at which you would expect skimmed milk to have a pH of 6.5. (2)

NEAB

5 The price £x of a certain cassette recorder is increased by £2 every six months. The number of recorders sold during the six months before the next increase is y thousand. The values covering 8 consecutive periods are shown in the table.

x	40	42	44	46	48	50	52	54
y	12.8	11.6	11.3	10.3	10.7	9.1	8.9	9.2

$[\sum x = 376, \sum x^2 = 17\,840, \sum y = 83.9, \sum y^2 = 893.33, \sum xy = 3898.4.]$

(i)   Plot a scatter diagram for the data. (3)

(ii) Obtain, in the form $y = a + bx$, the equation of the regression line of y on x, giving the values of a and b correct to 3 significant figures. Plot this line on your scatter diagram. (4)

(iii) Calculate an estimate of the number of recorders sold when the price is £58, and comment on the reliability of your estimate. (3)

(iv) Without further calculation, state whether the regression line of x on y will be the same as the line plotted in part (ii). Give a reason for your answer. (2)

UCLES

6 Students on a French course were given an oral test, a listening test and a written test. The test results for the eight students on the course are given in the table. For the oral test, students were given a grade on a scale ranging from A, through A–, B+, B etc down to D–. For the listening test they were given a mark out of 25, and for the written test they were given a mark out of 100.

Student	1	2	3	4	5	6	7	8
Oral test grade	C–	C+	B–	A–	C	B	D+	C
Listening test mark (x)	10	21	22	19	17	14	13	16
Written test mark (y)	34	76	74	60	68	44	45	53

$\sum x = 132 \quad \sum x^2 = 2296 \quad \sum y = 454 \quad \sum y^2 = 27\,402 \quad \sum xy = 7909$

(a) Calculate the value of the most appropriate measure of correlation between the results in the oral and listening tests, justifying your choice of measure. Interpret the value you obtain. (7)

(b) Calculate the value of the most appropriate measure of correlation between the results in the listening and written tests, justifying your choice of measure. Interpret the value you obtain. (5)

(c) The appropriate measure of correlation between the results in the oral and written tests has a value of 0.339. Comment on the indications given by the values of the three correlation coefficients about the performances of the students in the tests. (2)

NEAB

Hypothesis testing involves the testing of a **null hypothesis** (H_0) against an **alternative hypothesis** (H_1). The null hypothesis is constructed in such a way that a **test statistic** can be calculated to determine whether it is reasonable and should be **accepted** or whether there is **significant evidence** to reject it and accept the alternative hypothesis instead. Hypothesis tests can be two-tailed when looking for a change, such as testing $H_0 : \mu = 5$ against $H_1 : \mu \neq 5$, or one-tailed when looking for an increase (or decrease) such as testing $H_0 : \mu = 5$ against $H : \mu > 5$.

The **critical region** for a hypothesis test is the set of values of the test statistic for which the null hypothesis would be rejected. It is possible to make two statistical errors when carrying out a hypothesis test. We may reject a true null hypothesis (a Type I error) or we may accept a false null hypothesis (a Type II error). The **significance level** (or **size**) of a hypothesis test is the probability that the test statistic lies in the critical region if the null hypothesis is true, that is, the significance level is the probability of a Type I error. The **power** of a test is (1 – the probability of a Type II error), that is, the probability that a false null hypothesis is rejected.

The procedure to use when carrying out a hypothesis test is:

- Determine H_0, H_1 and the significance level.
- Decide whether a one- or two-tailed test is appropriate.
- Calculate the test statistic assuming H_0 is true.
- Compare the test statistic with the critical value(s) for the critical region.
- Accept or reject H_0 as appropriate.
- State conclusion in terms of the original problem.

For some hypothesis tests we need to use the *t*-distribution with υ degrees of freedom. If X follows such a distribution we write $X \sim t\,(\upsilon)$. For large values of υ the *t*-distribution is approximately the same as a Normal distribution with mean 0 and variance 1. You should check whether your examination board requires knowledge of this distribution and make sure that you can use the tables which go with it.

Some common hypothesis tests involving normal distributions include:

Test	Null hypothesis	Test statistic
A value x is from $X \sim N(\mu_0, \sigma^2)$ where σ^2 is known	$H_0 : \mu = \mu_0$	$\dfrac{X - \mu_0}{\sigma} \sim N(0, 1)$
A value x is from $X \sim B(n, p)$ (n large, p small, $np, nq > 5$)	$H_0 : \mu = np$	$\dfrac{X - np}{\sqrt{npq}} \sim N(0, 1)$ since $X \sim N(np, npq)$ approximately
A sample of size n with mean $\bar{x}$ is from $X \sim N(\mu_0, \sigma^2)$ where σ^2 is known	$H_0 : \mu = \mu_0$	$\dfrac{X - \mu_0}{\sigma / \sqrt{n}} \sim N(0, 1)$ because $\bar{X} \sim N(\mu, \dfrac{\sigma^2}{n})$
A sample with mean $\bar{x}$ is from $X \sim N(\mu_0, \sigma^2)$ where σ^2 is unknown and n is large	$H_0 : \mu = \mu_0$	$\dfrac{\bar{x} - \mu_0}{\hat{\sigma} / \sqrt{n}} \sim N(0, 1)$ because $\bar{X} \sim N(\mu, \dfrac{\sigma^2}{n})$ approximately where $\hat{\sigma}^2 = \dfrac{1}{n-1}\left(\Sigma x^2 - \dfrac{(\Sigma x)^2}{n} \right)$ is an estimate of σ^2

Test	Null hypothesis	Test statistic
A sample with mean $\bar{x}$ is from $X \sim N(\mu_0, \sigma^2)$ where σ^2 is unknown and n is small	$H_0 : \mu = \mu_0$	$\dfrac{\bar{x} - \mu_0}{\hat{\sigma}/\sqrt{n}} \sim t(n-1)$ where $\hat{\sigma}^2 = \dfrac{1}{n-1}\left(\Sigma x^2 - \dfrac{(\Sigma x)^2}{n}\right)$
That two samples with sizes n_1, n_2 and means $\bar{x}_1, \bar{x}_2$ are from Normal distributions with the same mean given that the variances of both parent distributions are equal to σ^2	$H_0 : \mu_1 = \mu_2$	$\dfrac{(\bar{x}_1 - \bar{x}_2) - (\mu_1 - \mu_2)}{\sigma\sqrt{1/n_1 + 1/n_2}} \sim N(0, 1)$
That two samples with sizes n_1, n_2 and means $\bar{x}_1, \bar{x}_2$ are from Normal distributions with the same mean given that the variances of the parent distributions are σ_1^2 are σ_2^2	$H_0 : \mu_1 = \mu_2$	$\dfrac{(\bar{x}_1 - \bar{x}_2) - (\mu_1 - \mu_2)}{\sqrt{\sigma_1^2/n_1 + \sigma_2^2/n_2}} \sim N(0, 1)$
That a sample with proportion of successes p_s is from a population with proportion of successes p_0 where the sample is large	$H_0 : p = p_0$	$\dfrac{p_s - p_0}{\sqrt{p_0 q_0/n}} \sim N(0, 1)$ where $q_0 = 1 - p_0$

It is possible to carry out a hypothesis test to determine whether the population correlation coefficient ρ is significantly different from zero (that is, whether there is a correlation between the two variables) based on the sample correlation coefficient r or r_s that has been calculated. You should ensure that you are familiar with the tables used by your examining board. Examples of hypotheses are given below:

Hypotheses	To test	Type of test
$H_0 : \rho = 0$, $H_1 : \rho \neq 0$	whether there is correlation	two-tail
$H_0 : \rho = 0$, $H_1 : \rho > 0$	whether there is positive correlation	one-tail
$H_0 : \rho = 0$, $H_1 : \rho < 0$	whether there is negative correlation	one-tail

If you need to revise this subject more thoroughly, see the relevant topics in the *Letts* A level Mathematics Study Guide.

For hypothesis tests concerning the Binomial and Poisson distributions it is easier to use a slightly different process which is best illustrated by an example.

Suppose that we are interested in whether a coin is fair or whether it favours heads. One experiment that could be carried out is to toss the coin ten times and record the number of heads. The number of heads would be our test statistic. Suppose further that we wish to carry out our test at the 5% significance level and that we obtain 8 heads in our experiment.

Our hypotheses would be $H_0 : p = \frac{1}{2}$ and $H_1 : p > \frac{1}{2}$, where p is the probability of the coin landing on heads. Since we are looking to determine whether the coin favours heads we are considering a one-tail test to see if the alternative hypothesis $p > \frac{1}{2}$ is more reasonable.

Now $P(X \geq 8)$ for a $B(10, \frac{1}{2})$ is 0.0547 from tables.

This means that 8 is not in the critical region as this would require $P(X \geq 8) < 0.05$.

Hence we accept H_0 and conclude that there is no significant evidence to suggest that the coin is not fair. A similar process can be carried out for two-tailed tests.

1 State, giving a reason in **each** case, whether the following statements regarding hypothesis tests are true or false.

(a) If the specified value of the significance level is decreased then the size of the critical region is also decreased. (2)

(b) If the value of the test statistic falls within the critical region then the null hypothesis **must** be false. (2)

NEAB

2 A particular investigation concentrated on people recently re-employed following a first period of unemployment. Each of a random sample of 50 such persons was asked the duration, in months, of this period of unemployment. A summary of the results is as follows:

Mean = 16.7 months   Variance = 193.21 months^2

Investigate at the 5% level of significance the claim that, for people re-employed after a first period of unemployment, the mean duration of unemployment is more than 12 months.

Indicate why, in carrying out your test, **no** assumption regarding the distribution of the duration of the first period of unemployment is necessary. (7)

NEAB

3 The breaking strength of a certain type of fishing line has a normal distribution with standard deviation 0.24 kN. A random sample of 10 lines is tested. The mean breaking strengths of the sample and of the population are $\bar{x}$ kN and μ kN respectively. The null hypothesis $\mu = 8.75$ is tested against the alternative hypothesis $\mu < 8.75$ at the $2\frac{1}{2}\%$ significance level.

(i) Show that the range of values of $\bar{x}$ for which the null hypothesis is rejected is given by $\bar{x} < 8.60$, correct to 2 decimal places. (3)

(ii) State the probability of making a Type I error. (1)

(iii) Find the probability of making a Type II error when $\mu = 8.50$. (4)

UCLES

4 In a national survey into whether low death rates are associated with greater prosperity, a random sample of 14 areas was taken. The areas, arranged in order of their prosperity, are shown in the table below together with their death rates. (The death rates are on a scale for which the 100 is the national average.)

most prosperous   least prosperous

Area	A	B	C	D	E	F	G	H	I	J	K	L	M	N
Death rate	66	76	84	83	102	78	100	110	105	112	122	131	165	138

(i) Calculate an appropriate correlation coefficient and use it to test, at the 5% level of significance, whether or not there is such an association. State your hypothesis and your conclusion carefully. (8)

(ii) A newspaper carried this story under the headline 'Poverty causes increased deaths'. Explain carefully whether or not the data justify this headline. (2)

(iii) The data include no information on the age distributions in the different areas. Explain why such additional information would be relevant. (2)

Oxford & Cambridge (MEI)

5 The proportion of patients who suffer an allergic reaction to a certain drug used to treat a particular medical condition is assumed to be 0.045.

(i) Each of a random sample of 90 patients with the condition is given the drug and X is the number who suffer an allergic reaction. Assuming independence, explain why X can be modelled approximately by a Poisson distribution and calculate $P(X = 4)$. (4)

(ii) When 400 patients were treated, 25 suffered an allergic reaction. Using a normal approximation, test at the 5% significance level whether the quoted figure of 0.045 is an underestimate. (7)

UCLES

6 The information on a match box states that the average contents of a box is 85 matches. The number of matches, x, in each of a random sample of 100 boxes was recorded and the following results calculated:

$$\Sigma x = 8460 \text{ and } \Sigma x^2 = 716\,400.$$

(a) Calculate an unbiased estimate, $\hat{\mu}$, of the mean μ of the contents of all such match boxes. (1)

(b) Show that the estimated standard error of $\hat{\mu}$ is approximately 0.263. (3)

(c) Test the null hypothesis that $\mu = 85$ against the alternative hypothesis that $\mu < 85$ at the 5 per cent level of significance. (4)

(d) Find, to two decimal plates, the power of the test if, in fact, $\mu = 84$. (4)

NEAB

7 A newspaper article claims that in newly married couples the husband is equally likely to be younger or older than the wife. In the past it was far more likely that the husband was older than the wife. A vicar wishes to investigate whether such a change as this has taken place and the therefore decides to test the claim made in the newspaper article.

(i) Letting p denote the probability that the husband is older than the wife, write down the null and alternative hypotheses which the vicar should use. Explain why the alternative hypothesis has the form it does. (3)

In the next month the vicar marries 19 couples and finds that in 14 of these marriages the husband is older than the wife.

(ii) Assuming the null hypothesis is true, find the probability of

(A) exactly 14 couples with the husband older that the wife,

(B) 4 or more couples with the husband older than the wife. (5)

(iii) The vicar carries out his test at the 5% level of significance. What conclusion should he reach and why? (3)

(iv) Give two objections (other than size) which might be raised against the vicar's sample. To what extent, if any, do these objections invalidate the vicar's test? (3)

Oxford &Cambridge (MEI)

8 A production line is designed to produce 13 amp fuses. In practice the fuses will blow at a level of current which is Normally distributed. A sample of 12 fuses is selected from the production line and tested to find the level of current at which they blow. The following values of the current at which they blow are recorded below:

13.102	12.971	13.053	13.056	13.173	12.548
13.060	13.193	13.187	13.300	13.168	13.132

Carry out a suitable test to decide whether the production line is producing fuses which will blow at 13 amps. (15)

NICCEA

A **Chi-squared** (χ^2) **test** is used to test for **goodness of fit** of observed data to certain probability distributions or for independence between two factors in a **contingency table.** Critical values for the calculated χ^2 statistic are given in tables for at least 10%, 5% and 1% significance levels. If these values are exceeded then the null hypothesis must be rejected.

The χ^2 distribution depends on a parameter υ (the number of degrees of freedom) which is calculated by subtracting one from the number of classes to ensure the total frequencies agree and by subtracting a further one for each statistic which is estimated from the observed data (for example, mean, variance, etc.) For an $m \times n$ contingency table there are $(m-1) \times (n-1)$ degrees of freedom.

Having calculated all necessary statistics from the observed data, the expected frequencies can be calculated using the assumptions of the null hypothesis (that is, that a certain distribution is followed for a goodness of fit test, or, independence for a test involving a contingency table).

It should be noted that **expected** frequencies must be at least 5 to use the χ^2 test. Adjacent classes (for a goodness of fit test) or similar rows/columns (for a test involving a contingency table) must be combined if necessary to ensure that this condition is satisfied before the test can be carried out. υ should be calculated *after* any combination has been done.

The χ^2 test statistic χ^2_{calc} is given by $\chi^2_{\text{calc}} = \sum \dfrac{(O-E)^2}{E}$

or the equivalent, but computationally easier, $\chi^2_{\text{calc}} = \sum \dfrac{O^2}{E} - N$

where N is the total frequency, O represents the observed frequencies and E the corresponding expected frequencies under the null hypothesis.

If $\upsilon = 1$ then **Yates' correction** must be used. This is $\chi^2_{\text{calc}} = \sum \dfrac{(|O-E|-0.5)^2}{E}$.

There is no equivalent computationally easier form in this case.

1 It is claimed that when homing pigeons are disorientated harmlessly they will exhibit no particular preference for any direction of flight after take-off. To test this, 128 pigeons, from lofts in a particular region, were disorientated harmlessly and then all released from a position 100 miles south of the region. The direction of flight of each pigeon was recorded with the following results.

Flight direction	$0° - 90°$	$90° - 180°$	$180° - 270°$	$270° - 360°$
Number of pigeons	30	35	36	27

Use the χ^2 goodness of fit test to determine whether or not these data can be used to discredit the claim.   (7)

NEAB

2 The following data are from the British Medical Journal. The table shows whether or not the subjects suffered from heart disease and how their snoring habits were classified by their partners.

	Never snores	Occasionally snores	Snores nearly every night	Snores every night
Heart disease	24	35	21	30
No heart disease	1355	603	192	224

(a) Use a χ^2 test, at the 5% significance level, to investigate whether frequency of snoring is related to heart disease.   (8)

(b) On the evidence above, do heart disease sufferers tend to snore more or snore less than others? Give a reason for your answer.   (2)

(c) Do these data show that snoring causes heart disease? Explain your answer briefly.   (2)

AEB

3 I kept a record for 100 days of the number of messages left on my answering machine after a day at work. I asked two students to propose suitable models for the data and to check the fit of their models using a chi-squared test. Pat proposed a Poisson model and Ben proposed a binomial model.

The data were as follows.

Number of calls	0	1	2	3	4	5	6 +
Frequency	6	18	30	21	16	9	0

(i) Carry out a chi-squared test for a Poisson distribution as proposed by Pat. Use the 5% level of significance.   (9)

(ii) Ben tested a binomial distribution with $n = 10$. He obtained a test statistic of 1.141, and the number of degrees of freedom was the same as for Pat's test. What conclusion should Ben have reached using the 5% level of significance?   (1)

(iii) Give one reason for preferring Pat's model and one reason for preferring Ben's.   (2)

Oxford & Cambridge (MEI)

4 A dentist notices that most people have cavities on the right-hand side of their mouths. He conjectures that this is because they are right-handed and as a result they clean the left side of their mouths more thoroughly.

To test his hypothesis he selects at random 30 right-handed and 20 left-handed patients and classifies them further on whether they have more cavities on the left or right side of their mouth.

Carry out a χ^2 test to find out whether there is sufficient evidence to support the dentist's claim. Use a 5% level of significance. (15)

NICCEA

	Side of the mouth with most fillings	
	Left	Right
Left-handed	12	8
Right-handed	7	23

5 As part of an investigation into colour associations, each child, in a random sample of 214 children, was asked to indicate which of the four listed emotions he or she associated most strongly with the colour red.

The response and the gender of each child was noted and the resultant data is summarised in the following contingency table.

Gender	Emotion indicated			
	Anger	Pain	Happiness	Love
Female	27	17	19	39
Male	34	28	12	38

(a) Test the hypothesis that there is no relationship between gender and the emotion associated most strongly with the colour red. (10)

(b) Investigate the claim that more than 30% of all children consider LOVE to be the emotion associated most with the colour red. (6)

NEAB

6 A company director monitored the number of errors on each page of typing done by her new secretary and obtained the following results.

No. of errors	0	1	2	3	4	5
No. of pages	28	73	65	49	25	10

(a) Show that the mean number of errors per page in this sample of pages is 2.

The director claims that the number of errors on a page can be modelled by a Poisson distribution.

(b) Test the director's claim using a 5% significance level.

Some time later the director notices that a 5 page report which the secretary has just typed contains only 4 errors.

(c) Stating your hypotheses clearly, test whether this represents evidence that the mean number of errors per page made by the secretary is now less than 2. (21)

London Examinations

10 *Estimation*

Estimates are used to try and obtain information about **population parameters** using **sample statistics.**

A **point estimate** seeks to provide a single value as an estimate for a population parameter. The best type of point estimate is one which is **unbiased**, that is, whose average value (or expected value) is the parameter it is trying to estimate. So if an estimate $\hat{\theta}$ for the parameter θ is needed we try and use one for which $E(\hat{\theta}) = \theta$. We also try and use an unbiased estimate for θ which has the smallest variance possible.

Common unbiased point estimates are:

Population parameter	Estimate
Population mean μ	$\hat{\mu} = \bar{X}$ (the sample mean)
Population variance σ^2	$\hat{\sigma}^2 = \dfrac{1}{n-1} \Sigma (X_i - \bar{X})^2$ $\equiv \dfrac{1}{n-1}\left[\Sigma X_i^2 - \dfrac{(\Sigma X_i)^2}{n} \right]$ $\equiv \dfrac{n}{n-1} \times \text{sample variance}$
Population proportion p	$\hat{p} = P_s$ (the sample proportion)

You should note that some examination boards use s^2 for $\hat{\sigma}^2$ whereas some examination boards use s^2 for the sample variances.

It is worth noting that different samples will give different estimates. Indeed when repeated samples are taken and a particular sample statistic calculated, these values form a new distribution called a **sampling distribution**. So, for example, the distribution formed when the sample means of all possible samples are calculated is called the sampling distribution of the mean.

An **interval estimate** seeks to provide an interval which contains a population parameter with a given probability. This probability is called the **confidence** associated with the interval and is usually given as a percentage hence the term **confidence interval**. As a reminder some of the common symmetrical 95% **confidence intervals** are given opposite:

**REVISION
SUMMARY**

Type of confidence interval	Form of confidence interval
Population mean based on a single value from a normal distribution with known variance σ^2	$x \pm 1.96\sigma$
Population mean based on a sample of size n with mean $\bar{x}$ from a normal distribution with known variance σ^2	$\bar{x} \pm 1.96\dfrac{\sigma}{\sqrt{n}}$
Population mean based on a large sample of size n with mean $\bar{x}$ from a normal distribution with unknown variance σ^2	$\bar{x} \pm 1.96\dfrac{\hat{\sigma}}{\sqrt{n}}$ where $\hat{\sigma}^2 = \dfrac{1}{n-1}\left[\sum x^2 - \dfrac{\left(\sum x\right)^2}{n}\right]$
Population mean based on a small sample of size n with mean $\bar{x}$ from a Normal distribution with unknown variance σ^2	$\bar{x} \pm t\dfrac{\hat{\sigma}}{\sqrt{n}}$ where $\hat{\sigma}^2 = \dfrac{1}{n-1}\left[\sum x^2 - \dfrac{\left(\sum x\right)^2}{n}\right]$ and t is the value from a $t(n-1)$ distribution such that $P(-t \le T \le t) = 0.95$
Population proportion based on a large sample of size n with sample proportion P_s	$P_s \pm 1.96\sqrt{\dfrac{P_s(1-P_s)}{n}}$

The number to replace the 1.96 for confidence intervals of different percentage confidences can be found from tables.

It should be noted that confidence intervals do not need to be symmetrical and you should ensure that you can deal with these as well.

The size of a confidence interval can be reduced in one of three ways:

(i)   Increasing the sample size.

(ii) Decreasing the percentage confidence.

(iii) Reducing the size of the population variance (if that is possible).

If you need to revise this subject more thoroughly, see the relevant topics in the *Letts* **A level *Mathematics Study Guide*.**

1 The mass of a certain brand of chocolate bar has a normal distribution with mean μ grams and standard deviation 0.85 grams. The masses, in grams, of 5 randomly chosen bars are

$$124.31, \qquad 125.14, \qquad 124.23, \qquad 125.41, \qquad 125.76.$$

Calculate a symmetric 90% confidence interval for μ, giving the end-points correct to 2 decimal places. (5)

Forty random samples of 5 bars are taken, and a 90% confidence interval for μ is calculated for each sample. Find the expected number of intervals that do not contain μ. (2)

UCLES

2 The random variables X and Y are independently distributed with means $(\mu - 1)$ and $(\mu + 1)$, respectively, and variances σ^2 and $2\sigma^2$, respectively. A single random observation is made of each of X and Y and the following three estimators for μ are proposed:

$$T_1 = \tfrac{1}{2}(X + Y), \qquad T_2 = \tfrac{1}{3}(2X + Y) \qquad \text{and} \qquad T_3 = \tfrac{1}{3}(2X + Y + 1)$$

(a) Show that **just two** of these estimators are unbiased for μ. (3)

(b) Show that **just two** of the estimators have the same variance. (3)

(c) Hence explain why T_3 is preferable to both T_1 and T_2 as an estimator for μ. (1)

NEAB

3 A bank posted a questionnaire to each of a random sample of 20 800 of its customers. Out of the 4850 returned questionnaires, 679 indicated that the customer was dissatisfied with one or more of the bank's services.

(a) Calculate the proportion of the returned questionnaires that indicated dissatisfaction. (1)

(b) The bank used this proportion to calculate an approximate symmetric 99% confidence interval for the proportion of all its customers who feel such dissatisfaction. Obtain this confidence interval. (4)

(c) Write down the assumption implied by the bank's action in using the proportion referred to in (a) as the basis for its confidence interval. State, with a reason, whether or not you think this assumption is likely to be justified. (2)

NEAB

4 The Editor of a Computer Games magazine undertakes a simple survey of the magazine's readership. She contacts a random sample of 100 teenagers who have a regular order for the magazine. 85 of the teenagers duly complete a questionnaire.

From the questionnaire returns, the editor calculates that the 95% confidence interval for the mean length of time spent playing computer games during the previous week is as follows:

$$414 \text{ minutes} \le \mu_c \le 450 \text{ minutes}.$$

Calculate the sample mean and standard deviation which the questionnaire provided. (8)

NICCEA

5 A firm has two machines, *A* and *B*, each of which fills cans with a soft drink. In order to compare the two machines, the volume, *x* ml, of drink dispensed by *A* in each of 20 randomly chosen cans, and the volume, *y* ml, of drink dispensed by *B* in each of 10 randomly chosen cans was measured. The following summarised results were obtained.

$$\Sigma x = 6771 \qquad \Sigma y = 3368$$

(a) For **each** machine, obtain an unbiased estimate of the mean volume of drink dispensed when filling cans. (2)

It is known that the volume of drink dispensed by each machine is normally distributed. It is also known that the standard deviation of the volume dispensed is 6.5 ml for machine *A* and 4.8 ml for machine *B*.

(b) Construct a symmetric 95% confidence interval for the difference between the mean volume dispensed by machine *A* and that dispensed by machine *B*. (4)

(c) Originally it was thought that the mean volume dispensed is the same for each machine. By considering your confidence interval state, with a reason, whether this belief should be amended. (2)

NEAB

6 An ambulance station services an area which includes more than 10 000 houses. It has been decided that if the mean distance of the houses from the ambulance station is greater than 10 miles then a new ambulance station will be necessary. The distance, *x* miles, from the station of each of a random sample of 200 houses was measured, the results being summarised by $\Sigma x = 2092.0$ and $\Sigma x^2 = 24\ 994.5$.

(i) Calculate, to 4 significant figures, unbiased estimates of

    (a) the population mean distance, μ miles, of the houses from the station, (1)

    (b) the population variance of the distances of the houses from the station. (2)

    State what you understand by the term 'unbiased estimate'. (1)

(ii) Using the sample data, a significance test of the null hypothesis $\mu = 10$ against the alternative hypothesis $\mu > 10$ is carried out at the $\alpha\%$ significance level. In the test, the sample mean is compared with the critical value of 10.65; as the sample mean is less than 10.65 the null hypothesis is not rejected. Calculate the value of α. (5)

(iii) Give a reason why it is not necessary for the distances to be normally distributed for the test to be valid. (1)

UCLES

7 A sample, of size 20, is selected from a population and the value of a particular variable is recorded for each member of the sample. The mean and variance for the sample are calculated and are found to be 59.4 and 196.74 respectively.

After further investigation of the sample it is realised that one of the values was mistakenly recorded as 96 instead of 69.

(i) Calculate the actual mean and variance of the 20 correct values. (9)

(ii) Using the correct statistics you have calculated in part (i), estimate the corresponding parameters for the population. (3)

NICCEA

8 When a darts player aims at the centre of the dart board the distance from the centre to the point where the dart lands is R, which is modelled as a continuous random variable. A suggested probability density function for R is as shown in the diagram.

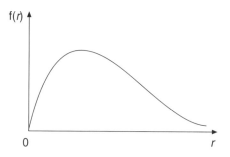

(i) Copy the diagram and show the position of the mode. Show also the approximate position of the mean in relation to the mode. (2)

The mean value of R will vary for players of different ability. The famous darts player Willy Jackson aims 50 darts at the centre of the board. The distances from the centre are summarised as follows.

$$\Sigma r = 35.5 \qquad \Sigma r^2 = 33.2$$

(ii) Construct a 90% confidence interval for the mean value of R. What assumption(s) have you made about the set of 50 throws? (5)

(iii) Estimate the number of throws required if the 90% confidence interval for the mean of R for Willy Jackson is to be of width 0.1. Explain why your answer is only an estimate. (4)

(iv) A second darts player records the results for 10 throws. Explain carefully why it would not be possible to obtain an accurate confidence interval for the mean value of R for this player. (3)

Oxford & Cambridge (MEI)

9 Solid fuel is packed in sacks which are then weighed on scales. It is know that if the full sack weights μ kg the weight recorded by the scales will be normally distributed with mean μ kg and standard deviation 0.36 kg.

A particular full sack was weighed 4 times and the weights recorded were

34.7,   34.4,   35.1   and   34.6 kg.

(a) Calculate a 95% confidence interval for the weight of this full sack. (5)

(b) State the width of the interval calculated in (a). (1)

(c) What percentage would be associated with a confidence interval of width 0.3 kg? (5)

(d) How many times would this full sack have to be weighed so that a 95% confidence interval for the weight would be of width 0.3 kg? (4)

AEB

Answers

1 DATA COLLECTION AND SAMPLING

Answer	Mark	Examiner's tip

1 (a) Number MPs 001–651. **1**

Select 103 three-digit random numbers ignoring 000 and those ≥ 652. **1**

Note the question made a specific request for the sampling frame to be identified.

Select corresponding MPs from numbered list of all MPs. This is the sampling frame. **1**

(b) Interviewers had to pick 1427 adults in the 103 constituencies so that they obtained a certain number in each of a number of categories, for example a certain number of men and women, certain numbers in different age groups, etc. **2**

You must refer to the quotation and try and give examples to show your understanding.

2 (a) (i) 1620, 9910 **1**

(ii) Use of random numbers or same sampling frame. **1**

Think about which managers can be selected. Given the nature of the question, lack of randomness is likely to be where the problem lies.

(iii) Only 0–9990 can be chosen. Only every tenth can be selected therefore not a random sample. **2**

(b) (i) 859 **1**

(ii) Allows every number in the range 0–11 999. **1**

Use part (a) (iii) as a starting point for your thinking as this is likely to be where improvement will take place.

(iii) Each manager does not have an equal chance of being chosen. **1**

3 (a) Select 20 four-digit random numbers. **1**

Ignore 0000 and those ≥ 2126. **1**

Outline the steps clearly making sure that you use the details given in the question.

Ignore repeats. **1**

This corresponds to 'without replacement'.

Number books 0001–2125 and choose books using selected random numbers. **1**

(b) (i) Popular books are more likely to be out on loan.

∴ Estimate will be too low. **2**

Say *how* the estimate is likely to be affected and *why*.

(ii) Newer books will have been borrowed on less occasions than they would have been in a full year.

∴ Estimate will be too low. **2**

(c) Borrowing patterns for fiction and non-fiction are not likely to be the same. **1**

(d) Select books from catalogue instead of from shelves to overcome the problem in (b)(i). **1**

Answer	Mark	Examiner's tip
Use an annual rate of borrowing to overcome the problem in (b)(ii).	1	
Use a stratified sample according to type of book e.g. fiction, scientific, historical, etc. if data is available. This overcomes the problem in (c).	2	To get maximum marks try and give suggestions as to what type of stratification can be used.

2 DATA PRESENTATION AND ANALYSIS

Answer	Mark	Examiner's tip
1 (i) Mean = $$\frac{6 \times 0 + 3 \times 1 + 1 \times 2 + ... + 1 \times 9 + 0 \times 10}{34}$$	1	Show your working to indicate a clear method.
$$= \frac{115}{34} = \underline{3.382} \text{ (correct to 3 d.p.)}$$	1	
Standard deviation = $$\sqrt{\frac{6 \times 0^2 + 3 \times 1^2 + 1 \times 2^2 + \cdots + 1 \times 9^2 + 0 \times 10^2}{34} - 3.382^2}$$	1	Show a clear method.
$$= \underline{2.327} \text{ (correct to 3 d.p.)}$$	1	
(ii) Mean of $A = 6$	2	The mean will be to the right of the middle since more values are to the right.
Mean of $B = 5$	1	
(iii) The standard deviation for A is larger than the standard deviation for B since the values are more spread out.	3	Make sure that you give your reasons.
(iv) Player A is better.	1	
Most skittles are knocked down with the first ball	2	Your reasons are vital here.
and as a result the second ball is low scoring.	1	
2 (a) Width per year = $\frac{0.5}{5} = 0.1\,\text{cm}$	1	Note that the width of the first class is 5 because it is age in *completed* years.
Frequency density in 1st class = $\frac{260}{5} = 52$ ∴ height is 1 cm per frequency density of 10 = 0.1 cm per frequency density of 1	1	Remember that height corresponds to frequency density, not frequency.
(i) Width = $(45 - 16) \times 0.1 = \underline{2.9\,\text{cm}}$	1	
Height = $\frac{1727}{45 - 16} \times 0.1 = \underline{6.0\,\text{cm}}$	1	
(ii) Width = $(80 - 65) \times 0.1 = \underline{1.5\,\text{cm}}$	1	
Height = $\frac{577}{80 - 65} \times 0.1 = \underline{3.8\,\text{cm}}$	1	

Answer	Mark	Examiner's tip

(b)

Mid-points	2.5	10.5	30.5	55	72.5	90
Frequencies	260	543	1727	756	577	135

3

Note again that the measurements are in completed years so that the boundaries are 0, 5, 16, 45, 65, 80.

$$\bar{x} = \frac{\sum fx}{\sum f}$$

$$= \frac{260 \times 2.5 + 543 \times 10.5 + \cdots + 577 \times 72.5 + 135 \times 90}{3998}$$

= <u>38.7 years (correct to 3 s.f.)</u>

2

3 (a) $\dfrac{101}{2} = 50.5$

1

(b)

$$\frac{50.5 - 38}{m - 0.5} = \frac{62 - 38}{1 - 0.5}$$

2

The method basically assumes a frequency polygon and equates two gradients.

$$m = 0.5 + \frac{50.5 - 38}{62 - 38} \times (1 - 0.5)$$

1

Rearrange the previous expression.

$$= 0.760 \text{ (correct to 3 d.p.)}$$

1

<u>Median time is 0.760 hours.</u>

(c) $\dfrac{86 + 98}{2} = 92\%$ are less than 3 hours.

1

Since 3 is halfway between 2 and 4, cumulative frequency is halfway between 86 and 98.

∴ <u>8% exceed 3 hours.</u>

1

4 (i)

	Q_1	Q_2	Q_3
Paper 1	26	38	56
Paper 2	47	63	75

2

Be careful to use the scale on the graph correctly to read off the medians and quartiles.

3

Use the same diagram so that both graphs can be compared easily.

(ii) Box plots give quick and direct comparison of quartiles and medians.

1

Try and think of how the two methods compare.

Cumulative frequency curves can be used to give information both ways round.

1

Answer	Mark	Examiner's tip

The cumulative frequency graph shows more information than that given by the box plot. **1**

5 (a) Pie chart. **1** Pie charts compare parts to the whole.

(b)

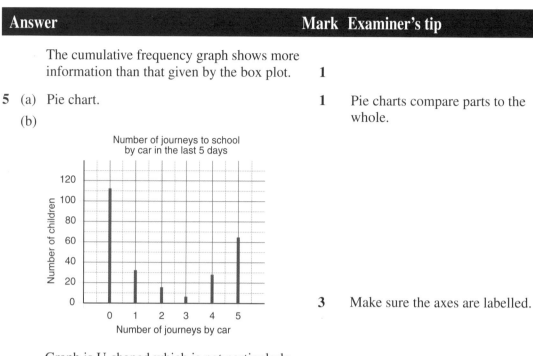

Number of journeys to school by car in the last 5 days

3 Make sure the axes are labelled.

Graph is U-shaped which is not particularly common. **1**

(c)

Time	Class width	Frequency	Frequency density
0.5 – 15.5	15	129	8.6
15.5 – 25.5	10	52	5.2
25.5 – 35.5	10	34	3.4
35.5 – 55.5	20	26	1.3
55.5 – 90.5	35	21	0.6

3 Remember that the vertical scale will be frequency density so that the areas are correct.

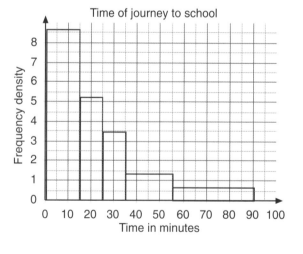

Time of journey to school

4 Remember that the horizontal axis has a scale on it and that the bars touch at common class boundaries.

6 (a) 11, 9, 8, 1 **2**

(b) Median is $\frac{1}{2}(65 + 1)$th = 33rd item so $Q_2 = 14$ **2**

Upper quartile is $\frac{3}{4}(65 + 1)$th = 49.5th item

so $\underline{Q_3 = 23}$ **2**

Answer	Mark	Examiner's tip

Lower quartile is $\frac{1}{4}(65 + 1)$th = 16.5th item

so $\underline{Q_1 = 6}$ **2**

(c) P_{67} is the $\frac{67}{100} \times 66 = 44.22 = $ 44th item i.e. $\underline{21}$. **2** Round to the nearest whole number to get the position of the required percentile.

(d), (f)

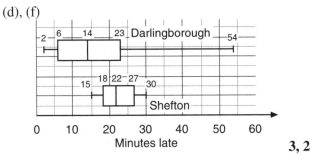

Make sure your scale is shown clearly.

Remember to use the same graph paper and scale and don't forget to say which is which!

3, 2

(e) $Q_3 - Q_2 > Q_2 - Q_1$ so the distribution is positively skewed. **1**

(g) Median lateness of trains from Darlingborough is less than that from Shefton. Both trains are likely to be late. Degree of lateness is less variable from Shefton than from Darlingborough. One fifth of all trains from Darlingborough are later than any train from Shefton. **4** Any sensible relevant comments would be allowed but do not repeat the same thing in different ways.

3 PROBABILITY

Answer	Mark	Examiner's tip

1 Required probability $= 0.96^4 \times 0.04$

$\quad\quad\quad\quad\quad\quad\quad = \underline{0.034}$ **2** We need the first 4 people to be ones whose names I don't know.

2 (i) We must require TTTTH if first head occurs on 5th throw.

$P(TTTTH) = (\frac{1}{2})^5 = \frac{1}{32}$ **1** Think about what must be true for situation to happen.

(ii) We require TTTTH or HHHHT.

$P(TTTTH \text{ or } HHHHT) = \frac{1}{32} + \frac{1}{32} = \frac{1}{16}$ **2** Use of addition rule with mutually exclusive events.

Answer	Mark	Examiner's tip

3 (a)

$$P(+) = P(D)\,P(+\,|\,D) + P(\overline{D})\,P(+\,|\,\overline{D})$$

$$= 0.03 \times 0.95 + 0.97 \times 0.01$$

$$= \underline{0.0382}$$

1
1
1

Use a tree diagram to think about what is going on.

D = disease
+ = result positive
− = result negative

(b) $$P(D\,|\,+) = \frac{P(D \cap +)}{P(+)} = \frac{P(D)(+\,|\,D)}{P(+)}$$

$$= \frac{0.03 \times 0.95}{0.0382} = \underline{0.746}$$

1

1

Use the conditional probability definition and the tree diagram.

4 (i) Required probability $= \frac{1}{900}$

1

(ii) Required probability $= 3! \times \frac{1}{900} = \frac{1}{150}$

2

The three numbers can be written in 3! arrangements each of which has the same probability.

(iii) Required probability $= \frac{6}{9} \times \frac{7}{10} \times \frac{7}{10}$

$$= \frac{49}{150}$$

2

1

There are 6 out of 9 possibilities for the first digit and 7 out of 10 for each of the second two.

(iv) Required probability $= \frac{1}{9} \times \frac{9}{10} \times \frac{9}{10}$

$$= \frac{9}{100}$$

3

1

There is only one choice for first digit but only one choice is not possible for the second and third digits.

(v) Required probability $= \frac{1}{9} \times \frac{9}{10} \times \frac{9}{10}$

$$+ \frac{8}{9} \times \frac{1}{10} \times \frac{9}{10} + \frac{8}{9} \times \frac{9}{10} \times \frac{1}{10}$$

$$= \frac{1}{4}$$

3

1

The plates must match only on the first digit *or* only on the second digit *or* only on the third digit.

5 (a)

M B

$27 - x$ x $20 - x$

22

Note the use of a Venn diagram to help start problem.

$$27 - x + 20 - x + x = 60 - 22$$

$$x = 9$$

2

M B

18   9   11

22

1

$$P(M \cap B) = \frac{9}{60} = \underline{\frac{3}{20}}$$

1

Answer	Mark	Examiner's tip

(b) $P(\bar{B}\,|\,M) = \dfrac{P(\bar{B} \cap M)}{P(M)}$ — **1** — A conditional probability is needed here which can be obtained using the conditional probability formula or directly from the Venn diagram.

$= \dfrac{\frac{18}{60}}{\frac{27}{60}} = \dfrac{18}{27} = \underline{\dfrac{2}{3}}$ — **2**

(c) $P(\bar{B}) = \dfrac{40}{60} = \dfrac{2}{3}$ — **1**

$P(\bar{B}) = P(\bar{B}\,|\,M)$ — **1** — Make a conclusion using your calculations.

∴ they are independent. — **1**

6 (a) Number of groups $= \begin{pmatrix} 8 \\ 3 \end{pmatrix} = \dfrac{8!}{3!5!} = \underline{56}$ — **2** — Order is not important as we are choosing groups.

(b) Number of ways of gaining no medals for

$Arrows = \begin{pmatrix} 6 \\ 3 \end{pmatrix} = \dfrac{6!}{3!3!} = 20$ — **1** — All must be won by others.

Number of ways of *Arrows* gaining at least 1 medal $= 56 - 20 = 36$ — **1** — Number of ways of *Arrows* winning at least one medal = Total number. of ways of medals being won – Number of ways of *Arrows* winning no medals.

Probability of *Arrows* winning at least one medal $= \frac{36}{56} = \underline{\frac{9}{14}}$ — **1**

7 (i) Number of ways $= \begin{pmatrix} 5 \\ 3 \end{pmatrix} = \dfrac{5!}{3!2!} = \underline{10}$ — **2**

(ii) Number of ways $= \begin{pmatrix} 6 \\ 4 \end{pmatrix} \times \begin{pmatrix} 5 \\ 3 \end{pmatrix}$ — **2** — The candidate answers 4 from *A* and 3 from *B* so *multiply* combinations.

$= \dfrac{6!}{4!\,2!} \times \dfrac{5!}{2!\,3!} = \underline{150}$ — **1**

(iii) Number of ways $= \begin{pmatrix} 5 \\ 3 \end{pmatrix} + \begin{pmatrix} 5 \\ 4 \end{pmatrix} + \begin{pmatrix} 5 \\ 5 \end{pmatrix}$ — **3** — The candidate either answers 3 out of 5 *or* 4 out of 5 *or* 5 out of 5 so add combinations.

$= \dfrac{5!}{3!\,2!} + \dfrac{5!}{4!\,1!} + \dfrac{5!}{5!\,0!} = \underline{16}$ — **1**

(iv) Number of ways $= \begin{pmatrix} 3 \\ 1 \end{pmatrix} \times \begin{pmatrix} 2 \\ 1 \end{pmatrix} \times \begin{pmatrix} 2 \\ 1 \end{pmatrix}$ — **4** — Candidate chooses 1 of the 3 sections to answer 2 questions and chooses 1 out of 2 questions in

$= 3 \times 2 \times 2 = \underline{12}$ — **1**

8 (a) (i) Required probability $= (0.35)^3$
$= \underline{0.0429}$ — **2** — Use multiplication since we require 1st goes straight on *and* 2nd goes straight on *and* 3rd goes straight on.

(ii) Required probability $= 0.45^3 + 0.2^3 + 0.35^3$
$= \underline{0.142}$ — **2** — *Either* all go left *or* all go right *or* all go straight on.

Answer	Mark	Examiner's tip

(iii) Required probability = $\binom{3}{2} \times 0.45^2 \times 0.2$

$= \underline{0.1215}$ **2**

There are $\binom{3}{2}$ ways of selecting which two go left.

(iv) Required probability
$= 3! \times 0.45 \times 0.2 \times 0.35 = \underline{0.189}$ **2**

There are 3! arrangements in which the three vehicles can go left, right and straight on.

(v) Required probability $= \binom{3}{2} \times 0.45^2 \times 0.55$

$= \underline{0.334}$ **2**

If two turn left the third must go 'not left'.

(b) Let X be the event all turn left, Y be the event all go in same direction.

We require $P(X \mid Y) = \dfrac{P(X \cap Y)}{P(Y)}$ **1**

$P(X \mid Y) = \dfrac{0.45^3}{0.45^3 + 0.2^3 + 0.35^3}$

$= \dfrac{0.45^3}{0.142}$ **2**

Use the answer from (a)(ii) in the denominator.

$= \underline{0.642}$ **1**

9 (i)

```
                            0.6      S (sugar)
                   D   <
                 (milk)
            0.7          0.4      S̄

                            0.25     S
                   L   <
            0.2  (lemon)
     <                      0.75     S̄

       0.1                  0.55     S
                   N   <
                (neither)
                            0.45     S̄
```
    3   Label the branches in a clear way.

$P(S) = P(M) P(S \mid M) + P(L) P(S \mid L)$
        $+ P(N) P(S \mid N)$

$= 0.7 \times 0.6 + 0.2 \times 0.25 + 0.1 \times 0.55$ **2**   Use the tree diagram to help you.

$= \underline{0.525}$ **1**

(ii) $P(M \cup S) = P(M) + P(S) - P(M \cap S)$ Addition law of probability.

$= 0.7 + 0.525 - 0.7 \times 0.6$ **2**

$= \underline{0.805}$ **1**

(iii) $P(M \cap S) = 0.7 \times 0.6 = \underline{0.42}$ **2**

$P(M \mid S) = \dfrac{P(M \cap S)}{P(S)} = \dfrac{0.42}{0.525}$ **2**   Use earlier result for $P(S)$.

$= \underline{0.8}$ **1**

4 DISCRETE RANDOM VARIABLES

Answer	Mark	Examiner's tip

1 (i) Let X be the number of sixes when a fair six-sided die is tossed.

$X \sim B(4, \frac{1}{6})$ — **1** — Define a letter to represent the random variable under

$$P(X = 1) = \binom{4}{1}\left(\frac{1}{6}\right)\left(\frac{5}{6}\right)^3$$

$= \underline{0.386 \text{ (correct to 3 d.p.)}}$ — **3**

(ii) $P(X \geq 1) = 1 - P(X = 0)$ — **1** — This is an important technique in this kind of problem.

$$= 1 - \binom{4}{0}\left(\frac{1}{6}\right)^0\left(\frac{5}{6}\right)^4$$ — **2**

$= 1 - 0.482\,25\ldots$ — **1**

$= \underline{0.518 \text{ (correct to 3 d.p.)}}$ — **1**

2 (i) Let X be number of calls in 30 minute period.

$X \sim Po(6)$ — **1**

$P(X = 4) = \dfrac{6^4\,e^{-6}}{4!} = \underline{0.134 \text{ (correct to 3 d.p.)}}$ — **2**

(ii) Let Y be number of calls in 15 minute period.

$Y \sim Po(3)$ — **1**

* $P(X > 3) = 1 - P(X = 0) - P(X = 1) - P(X = 2)$

$\quad - P(X = 3)$ — **2**

$= 1 - e^{-3} - \dfrac{3e^{-3}}{1!} - \dfrac{3^2 e^{-3}}{2!} - \dfrac{3^3 e^{-3}}{3!}$ — **2**

$= 1 - 0.647\,231\ldots$ — **2**

$= \underline{0.353}$ — **1**

* There is a much shorter alternative method using tables:

$P(X > 3) = 1 - P(X \leq 3)$ — **2**

$= 1 - 0.6472$ — **4** — Watch out for this as it will save

$= \underline{0.353}$ — **1** — you a lot of time.

3 (a) Let X be the number of breakdowns in a month.

$X \sim Po(2.5)$

$P(X = 3) = \dfrac{2.5^3 e^{-2.5}}{3!} = \underline{0.2138}$ — **1**

(b) Let Y be the number of breakdowns in three months.

$Y \sim Po(7.5)$ — **1**

$P(Y > 10) = 1 - P(Y \leq 10)$

$= 1 - 0.8622 = \underline{0.1378}$ — **2** — Use tables for $P(Y \leq 10)$

(c) We require $(a)^2 = 0.2138^2$ — Think carefully about what the

$= \underline{0.0457}$ — **2** — wording means.

Answer	Mark	Examiner's tip

4 Let R_i be the outcome i on the red die and B_j be the outcome j on the blue die.

$P(X = 4) = P(R_1 B_3 \cup R_2 B_2 \cup R_3 B_1)$

$\qquad = \frac{2}{6} \times \frac{3}{6} + \frac{2}{6} \times \frac{2}{6} + \frac{2}{6} \times \frac{1}{3} = \frac{12}{36} = \underline{\frac{1}{3}}$ **2**

There are only these three ways of getting a sum of 4.

Red

		1	2	3
	1	2	3	4
Blue	2	3	4	5 ← X values
	3	4	5	6

x	2	3	4	5	6
$P(X = x)$	$\frac{2}{36}$	$\frac{6}{36}$	$\frac{12}{36}$	$\frac{10}{36}$	$\frac{6}{36}$

2

Think about which combination of scores on the blue and red dice give each possible value of X.

$E(X) = 2 \times \frac{2}{36} + 3 \times \frac{6}{36} + 4 \times \frac{12}{36} + 5 \times \frac{10}{36} + 6 \times \frac{6}{36}$

$\qquad = \underline{4\frac{1}{3}}$ **2**

5 (i) Geometric with $p = \dfrac{1}{5}$ **1**

There is no upper limit to number of packets needed and p is constant. You should state any parameters.

(ii) $P(X = 3) = 0.8^2 \times 0.2 = \underline{0.128}$ **2**

(iii) $E(X) = \dfrac{1}{0.2} = \underline{5}$ **1**

Use standard results.

$\qquad Var(X) = \dfrac{1 - 0.2}{0.2^2} = \underline{20}$ **2**

(iv) $P(X > 4) = 0.8^4 \times 0.2 + 0.8^5 \times 0.2 + \ldots$ **1**

$\qquad = \dfrac{0.8^4 \times 0.2}{1 - 0.8} = \underline{0.4096}$ **1**

Use an infinite GP and its sum to infinity.

6 (a) Expected demand

$\qquad = 0 \times 0.05 + 1 \times 0.05 + 2 \times 0.10$

$\qquad + 3 \times 0.20 + 4 \times 0.15$

$\qquad = 5 \times 0.15 + 6 \times 0.15 + 7 \times 0.10 + 8 \times 0.05$ **1**

$\qquad = \underline{4.2}$ **1**

Make your working clear as the answer is given.

(b) (i) $Y = 3X - 1 \times (8 - X) = \underline{4X - 8}$ **1**

If X gateaux are sold there are $(8 - X)$ not sold at a loss of £1 each.

(ii) $E(4X - 8) = 4E(X) - 8 = 4 \times 4.2 - 8$

$\qquad = £8.80$ **2**

Remember we are talking money so an answer of 8.8 is not correct.

(c) Let U be number of gateaux sold.

$E(U) = 0 \times 0.05 + 1 \times 0.05 + 2 \times 0.10$

$\qquad + 3 \times 0.20 + 4 \times 0.15 + 5 \times 0.15$

$\qquad + 6 \times 0.30$

$\qquad = 4$ **1**

If the demand is 6, 7 or 8 only 6 gateaux are sold.

Answer	Mark	Examiner's tip

$$Y = 3U - (6 - U) = 4U - 6$$

1 — There are now $6 - U$ gateaux not sold.

$$E(Y) = 4E(U) - 6 = 4 \times 4 - 6 = \underline{£10}$$

1 — Remember that the answer is given – you must show your working clearly.

(d) (i) Expected profit goes up.

1 — Think about how your working earlier in the question may help.

    (ii) You may lose customers because you cannot satisfy demand.

1

7 Binomial with parameters n and p.   **1**

(a) Use B(20, 0.16)

$$P(0) = 0.84^{20} = \underline{0.0306}$$

$$P(1) = \binom{20}{1} 0.84^{19}\, 0.16 = \underline{0.1165}$$

$$P(2) = \binom{20}{2} 0.84^{18}\, 0.16^2 = \underline{0.2109}$$

$$P(3) = \binom{20}{3} 0.84^{17}\, 0.16^3 = \underline{0.2410}$$

4 — One mark for each.

(b) $P(4) = 1 - P(0) - P(1) - P(2) - P(3)$

$$= \underline{0.4010}$$

2 — If there are 4 or more requests he still sells only 4.

(c) Profit per paper sold = 30p
Loss per paper unsold = 20p
Let X = number of papers sold
Profit $= 30X \times - 20\,(4 - X) = 50X - 80$

1 — Losses are negative.

$$\begin{aligned} E(X) &= \sum x P(X = x) \\ &= 0 \times 0.0306 + 1 \times 0.1165 + 2 \times 0.2109 \\ &\quad + 3 \times 0.2410 + 4 \times 0.4010 \\ &= 2.8653 \end{aligned}$$

2

Expected profit $= E(50X - 80) = 50\,E(X) - 80$
$$= 50 \times 2.8653 - 80 = \underline{63p}$$

1 — Answer needs to be to the nearest penny.

8 (i)

r	−5	−4	−3	−2	−1	0	1	2	3	4	5
P($X = r$)	k	$2k$	$3k$	$4k$	$5k$	$6k$	$5k$	$4k$	$3k$	$2k$	k

2 — Tabulate $\equiv$ put in a table.

$$\sum P(X = r) = 1 \Rightarrow 36k = 1 \Rightarrow k = \tfrac{1}{36}$$

1 — This is an important principle.

1

Answer	Mark	Examiner's tip

(ii) $E(X) = 0$ (symmetry) **1**

$\quad Var(X) = E(X^2) - 0^2$

$\qquad = (-5)^2(k) + (-4)^2(2k) + (-3)^2(3k)$

$\qquad \quad + (-2)^2(4k) + (-1)^2(5k) + (0)(6k)$

$\qquad \quad + 1^2(5k) + 2^2(4k) + 3^2(3k)$

$\qquad \quad + 4^2(2k) + 5^2(k)$

$\qquad = 210k = \dfrac{35}{6}$ **1**

$\quad \sigma = \sqrt{Var(X)} = \sqrt{\dfrac{35}{6}} = \underline{2.415}$ **1**

Examiner's tip: Note hint in question of 'write down' and use of symmetry.

(iii) We need $P(X > 0) = 5k + 4k + 3k + 2k + k$

$\qquad\qquad\qquad\quad = 15k = \dfrac{15}{36} = \dfrac{5}{12}$ **2**

Examiner's tip: Try and relate the condition we require to the model.

(iv) Let Y_i be the event that the highest mark is not higher than a candidate's true ability warrants after i examinations.

We require

(A) $1 - P(Y_2) = 1 - \left(\tfrac{7}{12}\right)^2 = \underline{0.6597}$

(B) $1 - P(Y_4) = 1 - \left(\tfrac{7}{12}\right)^4 = \underline{0.8842}$ **3**

Examiner's tip: Very careful thought is needed to establish what is required here.

(v) The more times the examination is taken the greater the probability of performing better than true ability. **1**

The model assumes true ability does not increase and this may not be true. **1**

9 (a)

r	1	2	3
$P(R = r)$	$\tfrac{1}{6}$	$\tfrac{4}{6}$	$\tfrac{1}{6}$

2

g	1	2	3
$P(G = g)$	$\tfrac{2}{6}$	$\tfrac{2}{6}$	$\tfrac{2}{6}$

2

(b) $E(R) = 2 \quad E(G) = 2$ (symmetry) **2**

Examiner's tip: Notice words 'write down' and use of symmetry.

(c) $Var(R) = E(R^2) - \mu^2$

$\qquad = 1^2 \times \tfrac{1}{6} + 2^2 \times \tfrac{4}{6} + 3^2 \times \tfrac{1}{6} - 2^2$

$\qquad = \tfrac{26}{6} - 4 = \tfrac{2}{6} = \underline{\tfrac{1}{3}}$ **2**

$\quad Var(G) = 1^2 \times \tfrac{2}{6} + 2^2 \times \tfrac{2}{6} + 3^2 \times \tfrac{2}{6} - 2^2$

$\qquad = \tfrac{28}{6} - 4 = \tfrac{4}{6} = \underline{\tfrac{2}{3}}$ **2**

Examiner's tip: Note printed answer – you must show your working clearly.

Answer	Mark	Examiner's tip

(d) $E(3R + 2G) = 3E(R) + 2E(G)$

$= 3 \times 2 + 2 \times 2 = \underline{10}$ — **2**

$\text{Var}(3R + 2G) = 3^2\text{Var}(R) + 2^2\,\text{Var}(G)$

$= 9 \times \frac{1}{3} + 4 \times \frac{2}{3} = \frac{17}{3}$ — **2**

Remember:
$E(a\,X + b\,Y) = a\,E(X) + b\,E(Y)$

Remember:
$\text{Var}(aY + bX) = a^2\text{Var}(Y) + b^2\,\text{Var}(X)$

(e) Both give $E(T) = 10$ — **1**

$\text{Var}(5R) = \frac{25}{3}$ $\text{Var}(5G) = \frac{50}{3}$ — **1**

$\therefore$ choose $\alpha = 0$, $\beta = 5$ as this maximises variance. — **1**

5 CONTINUOUS RANDOM VARIABLES

Answer	Mark	Examiner's tip

1 For $-2 \le x \le 0$, $F(x) = \displaystyle\int_{-2}^{x}\left(\frac{1}{2} + \frac{1}{4}t\right)dt$

$= \left[\dfrac{t}{2} + \dfrac{t^2}{8}\right]_{-2}^{x}$ — **1**

$= \left(\dfrac{x}{2} + \dfrac{x^2}{8}\right) - \left(-1 + \dfrac{1}{2}\right)$

$= \underline{\dfrac{x}{2} + \dfrac{x^2}{8} + \dfrac{1}{2}}$ — **1**

$F(0) = \frac{1}{2}$ — **1**

For $0 < x \le 2$, $F(x) = \dfrac{1}{2} + \displaystyle\int_{0}^{x}\left(\frac{1}{2} - \frac{1}{4}t\right)dt$ — **1**

$= \dfrac{1}{2} + \left[\dfrac{t}{2} - \dfrac{t^2}{8}\right]_{0}^{x}$

$= \underline{\dfrac{1}{2} + \dfrac{x}{2} - \dfrac{x^2}{8}}$ — **1**

Don't forget the cumulative probability up to 0 given by $F(0)$.

2 (i) $P(X < 2) = P(0 \le x \le 1) + P(1 < x < 2)$

$= \displaystyle\int_{0}^{1}\frac{2}{5}x\,dx + \int_{1}^{2}\frac{1}{10}(5 - x)\,dx$ — **1**

$= \left[\dfrac{x^2}{5}\right]_{0}^{1} + \left[\dfrac{1}{10}\left(5x - \dfrac{x^2}{2}\right)\right]_{1}^{2}$

$= \dfrac{1}{5} + \left(\dfrac{8}{10} - \dfrac{9}{20}\right)$ — **1**

$= \underline{\dfrac{11}{20}}$ — **1**

Watch here that there are two parts to the calculation since $f(x)$ has different definitions for different x values.

Since this gives an exact decimal you could write 0.55 instead.

Answer	Mark	Examiner's tip

(ii) $E(X) = \int_0^1 x \cdot \frac{2}{5}x \, dx + \int_1^5 x \cdot \frac{1}{10}(5-x) \, dx$

Watch the two parts again.

$$= \int_0^1 \frac{2}{5}x^2 \, dx + \int_1^5 \frac{1}{10}\left(5x - x^2\right) dx$$

$$= \left[\frac{2}{15}x^3\right]_0^1 + \left[\frac{1}{10}\left(\frac{5}{2}x^2 - \frac{1}{3}x^3\right)\right]_1^5 \qquad \mathbf{1}$$

$$= \frac{2}{15} + \frac{1}{10}\left(\frac{125}{2} - \frac{125}{3} - \left(\frac{5}{2} - \frac{1}{3}\right)\right) \qquad \mathbf{1}$$

$$= \frac{2}{15} + \frac{1}{10}\left(\frac{120}{2} - \frac{124}{3}\right)$$

$$= 2 \qquad \mathbf{1}$$

The expected lifetime is 2000 hours.

3 (a)

Show scales on axes including units and also show key points such as where the density function meets the axes, maximum points, etc.

2

(b) Area under curve $= \frac{1}{2} \times 60 \times 40\lambda = 1200\lambda$ **1**

But area under curve = 1   **1**

$1200\lambda = 1 \Rightarrow \lambda = \frac{1}{1200}$ **1**

Note hint in question to help you – it is far easier than using integration here.

(c) (i) $F(40)$ = area between 0 and 40

= one third area of whole triangle

$= \frac{1}{3}$ **1**

(ii) $F(t) = \frac{1}{3} + \int_{40}^{t} \frac{1}{1200}(80 - x) \, dx$

$\qquad\qquad$ for $40 \le t \le 80$ **1**

Note use of a different letter (x) for variable to ensure an answer in terms of t.

$$= \frac{1}{3} + \left[\frac{-(80-x)^2}{2400}\right]_{40}^{t} \qquad \mathbf{1}$$

$$= \frac{1}{3} - \frac{(80-t)^2}{2400} + \frac{40^2}{2400}$$

$$= 1 - \frac{1}{2400}(80-t)^2 \text{ for } 40 \le t \le 80 \qquad \mathbf{1}$$

Since $\dfrac{40^2}{2400} = \dfrac{1600}{2400} = \dfrac{2}{3}$

Answer	Mark	Examiner's tip

(d) We require F(t) = 0.6 and for this $t \geq 40$.   **1**   Since $0.6 > \frac{1}{3}$ we know $t \geq 40$.

$$1 - \frac{1}{2400}(80 - t)^2 = 0.6$$ Solve for t.

$$\frac{(80 - t)^2}{2400} = 0.4$$

$$(80 - t)^2 = 960$$

$$80 - t = \pm \sqrt{960}$$

$t = 80 - \sqrt{960}$ since $t < 80$ **1**

$= 49.0161$ minutes   **1**   Change your answer into a time

i.e. <u>open tent at 3.19 pm.</u>   **1**   by adding 49 minutes onto 2.30 pm.

(e)

A curve is a more likely shape, mode still 40, since number of competitors taking ≥ 60 is likely to be small and so curve tails off.

1

4 (a) $P(T \leq 1) = F(1) = \frac{1}{2} - \frac{3}{16} = \frac{5}{16}$ **2**

(b) $F(1.23) = \frac{1}{2} \times 1.23^3 - \frac{3}{16} \times 1.23^4 = 0.50127$ **1**

$F(1.22) = \frac{1}{2} \times 1.22^3 - \frac{3}{16} \times 1.22^4 = 0.49255$ **1**

<u>Since one is above and one below 0.5,</u>   State your conclusion based on
<u>the median is in range $1.22 < m < 1.23$</u>   **1**   your calculations.

(c) $f(t) = F'(t)$

$$= \begin{cases} \dfrac{3t^2}{2} - \dfrac{12t^3}{16} = \dfrac{3t^2}{2} - \dfrac{3t^3}{4} & 0 \leq t \leq 2 \\ 0 & \text{otherwise} \end{cases}$$ **3**   Differentiate the cumulative distribution to get the probability density function.

(d) Modal time is when $f'(t) = 3t - \dfrac{9t^2}{4} = 0$ **1**   This is an important principle.

i.e. when $3t\left(1 - \dfrac{3t}{4}\right) = 0$

$t = \frac{4}{3}$ minutes   **2**

(e)

Mark some points on the axes to locate the curve and show its features.

2

Answer	Mark	Examiner's tip

(f) On a windy day the taper is likely to go out more quickly i.e. peak of curve will be nearer 0. | 1 | Try and relate 'real-life' to what will happen in the model.

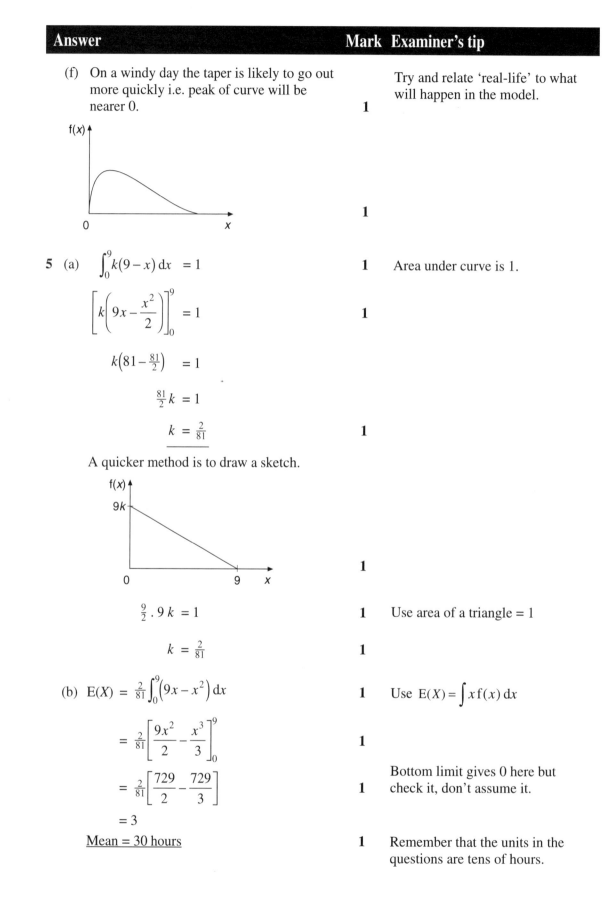

| | 1 | |

5 (a) $\int_0^9 k(9-x)\,\mathrm{d}x = 1$ | 1 | Area under curve is 1.

$$\left[k\left(9x - \frac{x^2}{2}\right)\right]_0^9 = 1$$ | 1 |

$$k\left(81 - \tfrac{81}{2}\right) = 1$$

$$\tfrac{81}{2}k = 1$$

$$k = \tfrac{2}{81}$$ | 1 |

A quicker method is to draw a sketch.

| | 1 | |

$$\tfrac{9}{2}\cdot 9\,k = 1$$ | 1 | Use area of a triangle = 1

$$k = \tfrac{2}{81}$$ | 1 |

(b) $\mathrm{E}(X) = \tfrac{2}{81}\int_0^9 \left(9x - x^2\right)\,\mathrm{d}x$ | 1 | Use $\mathrm{E}(X) = \int x\,\mathrm{f}(x)\,\mathrm{d}x$

$$= \tfrac{2}{81}\left[\frac{9x^2}{2} - \frac{x^3}{3}\right]_0^9$$ | 1 |

$$= \tfrac{2}{81}\left[\frac{729}{2} - \frac{729}{3}\right]$$ | 1 | Bottom limit gives 0 here but check it, don't assume it.

$$= 3$$

<u>Mean = 30 hours</u> | 1 | Remember that the units in the questions are tens of hours.

Answer	Mark	Examiner's tip

(c) $\sigma^2 = E(X^2) - \mu^2$

$\qquad = \frac{2}{81}\int_0^9 \left(9x^2 - x^3\right) dx - 3^2$ **1**   Use $E(X^2) = \int x^2 f(x)\, dx$

$\qquad = \frac{2}{81}\left[\dfrac{9x^3}{3} - \dfrac{x^4}{4}\right]_0^9 - 9$ **1**

$\qquad = \frac{2}{81}\left[\dfrac{6561}{3} - \dfrac{6561}{4}\right] - 9$

$\sigma^2 = 4.5$ **1**

$\sigma = \sqrt{4.5} = 2.1213$ Remember that we are in tens of
Standard deviation is 21.2 hours.   **1**   hours again.

(d) $P(X \le 5) = \frac{2}{81}\int_0^5 (9 - x)\, dx$ **1**   Remember upper limit is 5 *not* 50.

$\qquad = \frac{2}{81}\left[9x - \dfrac{x^2}{2}\right]_0^5$ **1**

$\qquad = \frac{2}{81}\left(45 - \frac{25}{2}\right) = \frac{65}{81}$ **1**   Leave your answer as a fraction –
it is exact.

(e) Probability that both work for more than
50 hours

$\qquad = \left(1 - \dfrac{65}{81}\right)^2 = \underline{0.0390}$ **2**

(f) There is a fixed upper limit for the lifetime and   Any sensible, relevant comment
this is not realistic.   **1**   would be accepted.

6 (a) Required probability = 0   **1**   Remember that continuous distributions give probabilities of ranges
(b) $P(X < 180) = \int_0^{180} \frac{1}{90} e^{-\frac{1}{90}x}\, dx$ of values not single value.

$\qquad = \left[-e^{-\frac{1}{90}x}\right]_0^{180}$ **1**

$\qquad = 1 - e^{-2} = \underline{0.865}$ **1**

(c) $P(X > 120) = \int_{120}^{\infty} \frac{1}{90} e^{-\frac{1}{90}}\, dx$

$\qquad = \left[-e^{-\frac{1}{90}x}\right]_{120}^{\infty}$ **1**

$\qquad = e^{\frac{-120}{90}} = \underline{0.264}$ **1**

6 THE NORMAL DISTRIBUTION

Answer	Mark	Examiner's tip

1 (a) It is a common naturally occurring distribution. **1**

Tables allow calculations based on it to be performed easily. **1**

(b) $P(X < 240) = P\left(Z < \dfrac{240 - 246}{5}\right)$ **1**

$= P(Z < -1.2)$ **1**

$= 1 - P(Z < 1.2)$

$= 0.1151$

<u>Required percentage is 11.5%.</u> **1**

Note that the question asks for a percentage answer.

2 The number of sixes, X, follows a $B(900, \frac{1}{6})$ distribution.

$E(X) = np = \frac{900}{6} = 150$ so a Normal approximation

is appropriate i.e. $X \sim N(150, 125)$ **1**

$P(X \geq 160) = P(X > 159.5)$

$\qquad = P\left(Z > \dfrac{159.5 - 150}{\sqrt{125}}\right)$ **1**

Notice that a continuity correction is needed.

$\qquad = P(Z > 0.849)$ **1**

$\qquad = 1 - P(Z < 0.849)$ **1**

$\qquad = 1 - \{0.7995 + \frac{9}{10}(0.8023 - 0.7995)\}$

$\qquad = \underline{0.198}$ **1**

Use the fact that the area under the curve is 1 to change to a probability that can be obtained from tables using interpolation.

3 (a) Binomial distribution with $n = 5000$ $p = 0.0004$ **1**

$np = 2$ so use Poisson distribution with mean 2 since mean is small **2**

Make sure you know when to use each type of approximation.

(b) Poisson distribution with $\mu = 0.65$ **1**

Mean for 50 m² of carpet $= 50 \times 0.65 = 32.5$ so use Normal distribution with mean and variance 32.5 since mean is large. **2**

4 (a) Total weight

$T \sim N(3 \times 80 + 4 \times 56, 3 \times 12^2 + 4 \times 6^2)$

$T \sim N(464, 576)$ **2**

Note that when adding the weights of three people the variance is $3s^2$ not $9s^2$.

$P(T > 500) = P\left(Z > \dfrac{500 - 464}{\sqrt{576}}\right) = P(Z > 1.5)$

Note $\sigma = \sqrt{576}$ on bottom of fraction.

$\qquad\qquad = 1 - P(Z < 1.5)$ **1**

$P(T > 500) = 1 - 0.933 = \underline{0.067}$ **1**

(b) $D = $ Men's weight – women's weight

$\sim N(3 \times 80 - 4 \times 56, 3 \times 12^2 + 4 \times 6^2)$

$D \sim N(16, 576)$ **2**

Note variance is $n_1\sigma_1^2 + n_2\sigma_2^2$ not $n_1\sigma_1^2 - n_2\sigma_2^2$

Answer	Mark	Examiner's tip

We need $P(D > 0) = P\left(Z > \dfrac{0-16}{\sqrt{576}}\right)$

$= P(Z > -0.67)$ **1**   Note the use of the symmetry of the curve here.

$= P(Z < 0.67) = \underline{0.75}$ **1**

5 (a) (i) $P(X \geq 3) = 1 - P(X \leq 2)$

$= 1 - \left[e^{-2.8} + 2.8e^{-2.8} + \dfrac{2.8^2 e^{-2.8}}{2!} \right]$ **1**

$= \underline{0.531}$ **1**

(ii) Number of letters received on 10 successive days follows a Poisson distribution with mean 28   **1**   Use the additive property for independent Poisson distributions.

A normal approximation N(28, 28) is appropriate since the mean is large.   **1**

$P(X \geq 30) = P(X > 29.5)$ **1**   We need to use a continuity correction.

$= P\left(Z > \dfrac{29.5 - 28}{\sqrt{28}}\right)$

$= P(Z > 0.283)$ **1**

$= 1 - P(Z < 0.283)$ **1**

$= 1 - \left[0.6103 + \tfrac{3}{10}(0.6141 - 0.6103) \right]$ Use linear interpolation if using tables which give values for z values of 2 decimal places.

$= \underline{0.389}$ **1**

(b) Mean is not likely to be constant.   **1**

More letters received at certain times of the year e.g. Christmas.   **1**   Give a reason for your answer.

6 (i)

3

(ii) $\dfrac{104 - \mu}{\sigma} = 1.751 \Rightarrow \mu + 1.751\sigma = 104$ (1)   You will probably need to use the Normal tables in reverse together with linear interpolation to get these.

$\dfrac{80 - \mu}{\sigma} = -2.054 \Rightarrow \mu - 2.054\sigma = 80$ (2)   **2**

$(1) - (2)$ gives $3.805\sigma = 24 \Rightarrow \underline{\sigma = 6.307}$ **1**   Solve as simultaneous equations.

$\therefore \underline{\mu = 92.96}$ **1**   Check your answers in both equations

Answer	Mark	Examiner's tip

(iii) We require $P(T > 100) = P\left(Z > \dfrac{100 - 94.5}{5.7}\right)$ **1**

     $= P(Z > 0.965)$ **1**

     $= 1 - P(Z < 0.965) = 0.167$

     <u>So 16.7% of sensors will work a 100°C.</u>   **1**

(iv) $P(Z > -2.3263) = 0.99$ **1**   You will probably be able to get this directly from tables.

     The temperature t we require satisfies

     $\dfrac{t - 94.5}{5.7} = -2.3263$ **2**

           <u>$t = 81.24°C$</u>   **1**

7   (i) $E(X) = \displaystyle\int_0^8 x \cdot \tfrac{3}{1024} x(x-8)^2 \, dx$

       $= \tfrac{3}{1024} \displaystyle\int_0^8 \left(x^4 - 16x^3 + 64x^2\right) dx$

       $= \tfrac{3}{1024} \left[\dfrac{x^5}{5} - 4x^4 + \tfrac{64}{3} x^3\right]_0^8$ **1**

       $= \underline{3.2}$ **1**

     $E(X^2) = \tfrac{3}{1024} \displaystyle\int_0^8 \left(x^5 - 16x^4 + 64x^3\right) dx$ Use $E(X^2) = \displaystyle\int x^2 \, f(x) \, dx$.

         $= \tfrac{3}{1024} \left[\tfrac{1}{6} x^6 - \tfrac{16}{5} x^5 + 16x^4\right]_0^8$ **1**

         $= 12.8$ **1**

     $\mathrm{Var}(X) = E(X^2) - E^2(X) = 12.8 - 3.2^2 = \underline{2.56}$ **1**

(ii)   f(t)

     0   2   10 t **1**   Graph is moved 2 to the right.

Length of appointments is between 2 and 10 minutes.   **1**

The doctor is most likely to spend 5 minutes with a patient.   **1**

(iii) Let Y be the time taken for 24 appointments

     By the Central Limit Theorem,

     $Y \sim N(24 \times (3.2 + 2), 24 \times 2.56)$ Don't forget to add 2 to the mean

     i.e. $Y \sim N(124.8, 61.44)$ **3**   of X to get the mean of Y.

     $P(Y < 120) = \dfrac{120 - 124.8}{\sqrt{61.44}}$ **1**   Don't forget to change 2 hours to minutes.

     $= P(Z < -0.612) = 1 - P(Z < 0.612)$ **1**

     $= 1 - (0.7291 + \tfrac{2}{10}(0.7324 - 0.7291))$

     $= \underline{0.270}$ **1**

Answer	Mark	Examiner's tip

8 (a) (i) Let X be the weight of a tin

$\therefore X \sim N(1000, 12^2)$

$P(X < 985) = P\left(Z < \dfrac{985 - 100}{12}\right)$ — 1

$= P(Z < -1.25)$ — 1

$= 1 - P(Z < 1.25) = \underline{0.1056}$ — 1

Be careful to work in grams throughout to be consistent in units.

(ii) $P(970 < x < 1015)$

$= P\left(\dfrac{970 - 1000}{12} < Z < \dfrac{1015 - 1000}{12}\right)$ — 1

$= P(-2.5 < Z < 1.25)$ — 1

$= P(Z < 1.25) - P(Z < -2.5)$

$= P(Z < 1.25) - (1 - P\{Z < 2.5\})$

$= 0.8944 - (1 - 0.9938) = \underline{0.8882}$ — 1

Make sure that you can deal with all the different types of calculations of this form.

(b) Let W be the weight of a tin $\therefore W \sim N(\mu, 12^2)$

$P(W < 1000) = 0.01$

$\therefore \quad P\left(Z < \dfrac{1000 - \mu}{12}\right) = 0.01$ — 2

So $\dfrac{1000 - \mu}{12} = -2.3263$ — 1

$\underline{\mu = 1027.9}$ — 1

Make sure you don't forget the minus sign.

(c) Let B be weight of the box. The total weight T is given by

$T = X_1 + X_2 + X_3 + X_4 + X_5 + X_6 + B$ — 1

$E(T) = 6\,E(X) + E(B) = 6 \times 1000 + 250$

$= 6250$ — 2

$Var(T) = 6\,Var(X) + Var(B) = 6 \times 12^2 + 10^2$

$= 964$ — 2

A common mistake here is to consider $6X + B$.

Remember that you are dealing with variances *not* standard deviations.

$P(T < 6200) = P\left(Z < \dfrac{6200 - 6250}{\sqrt{964}}\right)$ — 1

$= P(Z < -1.610)$

$= 1 - P(Z < 1.61) = 1 - 0.9463 = \underline{0.0537}$ — 1

Remember that the standard deviation is $\sqrt{964}$.

7 BIVARIATE DATA

Answer	Mark	Examiner's tip

1 (i) (a) Coefficient for $P = -1$ — 1 — Correlation is perfect negative.

Answer	Mark	Examiner's tip
(b) Coefficient for $R = 1$	1	Correlation is perfect positive. Don't be worried by the shallow angle of the line. The points do lie on a straight line which is the important thing.
(ii) The data sets are P and Q.	1	In both cases an increase in x always result in a decrease in y.

2 (i) $r = \dfrac{S_{xy}}{\sqrt{S_x S_y}} = \dfrac{\sum xy - \dfrac{(\sum x)(\sum y)}{n}}{\sqrt{\sum x^2 - \dfrac{(\sum x)^2}{n}}\sqrt{\sum y^2 - \dfrac{(\sum y)^2}{n}}}$

$$= \dfrac{6425 - \dfrac{76 \times 913}{12}}{\sqrt{560 - \dfrac{76^2}{12}}\sqrt{75153 - \dfrac{913^2}{12}}}$$ **1**   Show your method clearly.

$$= \dfrac{642.\dot{6}}{\sqrt{78.\dot{6}}\sqrt{5688.91\dot{6}}}$$ **1**   Show intermediate working in case you make a slip.

$$= \underline{0.961} \text{ (correct to 3 d.p.)}$$ **1**

| (ii) There is a strong linear relationship between x and y. | 1 | Try to avoid just repeating the phrase correlation as you are not telling the examiner anything. |
| (iii) The new value is 0.986 since the ranks do not change. | 2 | Adding a constant to all the data values does not change the rankings. |

3 (i) $(\bar{x}, \bar{y})$ satisfies both regression lines so   **1**   This is a crucial property
  $\bar{y} = -7 \times 21 + 163$ **1**
  $\underline{= 16}$ **1**

(ii) $(\bar{x}, \bar{y})$ satisfies the first regression line so
  $16 = -\frac{1}{7} \times 21 + c$ **1**
  $\underline{c = 19}$ **1**

(iii) Using the x on y regression line which can be
  rearranged as $x = \dfrac{163 - y}{7}$, we obtain   —   To estimate a x-value use the x on y line.
  $x = \dfrac{163 - 128}{7} = 5$ **2**

(iv) For positive correlation the regression line must have positive gradient.   **1**   The regression lines have negative gradient.

Answer	Mark	Examiner's tip

(v) Since $|r|$ is small there is little linear correlation so a regression line would not give a very reliable value since the pattern is not strongly linear.
2

You need to explain why you think the estimate is not reliable.

4 (a) The pH value of skimmed milk decreases as the temperature increases.
1

There appears to be a linear relationship between the pH value of skimmed milk and temperature.
1

Two comments are likely to be needed for 2 marks.

(b) $y = a + bx$

where $b = \dfrac{S_{xy}}{S_{xx}} = \dfrac{3291.88 - \dfrac{511 \times 78.52}{12}}{28\,949 - \dfrac{511^2}{12}}$
2

$= -0.007\,20$ (correct to 3 s.f.)
1

$a = \bar{y} - b\bar{x} = \dfrac{78.52}{12} - (-0.007\,20) \times \dfrac{511}{12}$

$= 6.85$ (correct to 3 s.f.)
1

$\underline{y = 6.85 - 0.007\,20x}$
1

(c) b is decrease in pH per °C increase in temperature.

a is the pH at temperature $0°C$
2

These must be in context – gradient and y-intercept are not enough.

(d) When $x = 20$, $y = 6.71$. $x = 20$ is within the given data range so this estimate is likely to be reliable.
2

This is a common type of question.

When $x = 95$, $y = 6.17$. $x = 95$ is outside the given data range so this estimate is not reliable as the pattern may change.
2

(e) $6.5 = 6.85 - 0.007\,20x \Rightarrow x = \dfrac{6.85 - 6.5}{0.007\,20}$

$= \underline{48.6°C}$
2

Because there is a strong linear relationship you can use the line of y on x to find x. (Usually you should use the x on y regression line.)

5 (i)

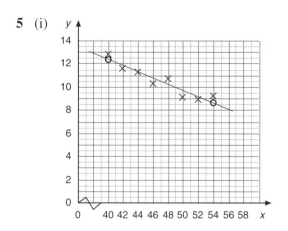

3

Choose sensible scales.

Answer	Mark	Examiner's tip

(ii) $b = \dfrac{S_{xy}}{S_{xx}} = \dfrac{3898.4 - \dfrac{376 \times 83.9}{8}}{17\,840 - \dfrac{376^2}{8}}$

Show your working clearly.

$\qquad = \dfrac{-44.9}{168} = -0.267$ (correct to 3 s.f.)   **2**

$a = \bar{y} - b\bar{x} = \dfrac{83.9}{8} - (-0.267) \times \dfrac{376}{8}$

$\qquad = 23.0$ (correct to 3 s.f.)   **1**

$\underline{y = 23.0 - 0.267x}$

Regression line on diagram.   **1**

Use two x-values to work out corresponding y-values and plot.

(iii) $y = 23.0 - 0.267 \times 58 = 7.514$ **1**

So <u>7514 recorders would be sold.</u>   **1**

Remember y is in thousands.

58 is outside data range so value not reliable as pattern may not continue to be the same.   **1**

This is a common type of question.

(iv) It will not because the points do not lie exactly on a straight line i.e. correlation is not perfect.   **2**

The two regression lines are only the same when correlation is perfect.

6 (a)

	Student	1	2	3	4	5	6	7	8
Rank	Oral	7	4	3	1	5.5	2	8	5.5
	Listening	8	2	1	3	4	6	7	5
	d	1	−2	−2	2	−1.5	4	−1	−0.5

   2

Note that we have tied ranks so we take the mean of the ranks they would otherwise have obtained.

$\sum d^2 = 32.5$ **1**

$r_s = 1 - \dfrac{6\sum d^2}{n(n^2 - 1)} = 1 - \dfrac{6 \times 32.5}{8(64 - 1)} = 0.613$ **2**

There is little correlation between oral result and listening test results.   **1**

A rank correlation coefficient is appropriate because Oral grades are not normally distributed.   **1**

This is a crucial point.

(b) $r = \dfrac{S_{xy}}{\sqrt{S_{xx}S_{yy}}}$

$\qquad = \dfrac{7909 - \dfrac{132 \times 454}{8}}{\sqrt{\left(2296 - \dfrac{132^2}{8}\right)\left(27\,402 - \dfrac{454^2}{8}\right)}}$ **1**

$\qquad = \dfrac{418}{\sqrt{118 \times 1637.5}} = 0.951$ **2**

Answer	Mark	Examiner's tip
Both sets of marks could be reasonably assumed to follow a Normal distribution.	1	This is the assumption.
r suggests a very strong linear relationship.	1	This is the conclusion.
(c) Students tend to achieve to a similar standard on both listening and written papers but there is not too much relationship between their performance on these and on the oral test.	2	Make sure that you relate this back to the context of the question.

8 HYPOTHESIS TESTING

Answer	Mark	Examiner's tip
1 (a) True, because the probability of a value being in the critical region has been reduced so the critical region must have become smaller.	2	
(b) False. There is still a small chance that the null hypothesis could be true namely the value of the significance level.	2	These two points are fundamentally important.

2 $H_0 : \mu = 12 \quad H_1 : \mu > 12$ — Mark 1 — Note we are looking for an increase.

$$Z_{test} = \frac{16.7 - 12}{\frac{\sqrt{193.21}}{\sqrt{50}}} = 2.391$$

Mark 2 — The standard error of the mean is $\frac{\sigma}{\sqrt{n}}$.

The critical value at the 5% level of significance is 1.6449 — Mark 1 — This is a one-tail test.

$Z_{test} > 1.6449$ so we reject H_0 and conclude that there is significant evidence to believe that the mean is more than 12 months. — Mark 2 — State your conclusion clearly in terms of the original problem.

The Central Limit Theorem means that the distribution of the sample mean can be assumed to be approximately Normal if *n* is large. — Mark 1 — Watch out for the Central Limit Theorem as it can prove vital in answering questions.

3 (i) $H_0 : \mu = 8.75 \quad H_1 : \mu < 8.75$
The critical value is *x* where

$$\frac{x - \mu}{\sigma / \sqrt{n}} = -1.96$$

Mark 1 — Don't forget the $\sqrt{n}$ as we are dealing with the standard error of the mean. The critical *z*-value is −1.96 because we are dealing with a one-tail test looking for a decrease.

$$x = 8.75 - 1.96 \times \frac{0.24}{\sqrt{10}}$$

Mark 1

$$= 8.60 \text{ (correct to 2 d.p.)}$$

Mark 1 — This is a printed answer so working must be clear.

(ii) Required probability = 0.025 — Mark 1 — This is the significance level of the test.

Answer	Mark	Examiner's tip

(iii) P(Type II error)

$= $ P (Accepting $H_0 \mid H_1$ true)

$= $ P($\bar{X} > 8.60$)   **1**

$= $ P$\left(Z > \dfrac{8.60 - 8.50}{0.24/\sqrt{10}} \right)$ **1**

$= $ P($Z > 1.318$)

$= 1 - $ P($Z < 1.318$)   **1**

$= 1 - \{0.9049 + 0.8\,(0.9066 - 0.9049)\}$

$= \underline{0.0937}$ **1**

Make sure that you understand what Type I and Type II errors are and how to calculate them.

We assume $\mu = 8.5$ under H_1.

4 (i) Ranks

Property	1	2	3	4	5	6	7	8	9	10	11	12	13	14
Death rate	1	2	5	4	7	3	6	9	8	10	11	12	14	13
d	0	0	2	0	2	−3	−1	1	−1	0	0	0	1	−1

1

$$\sum d^2 = 0^2 + 0^2 + 2^2 + 0^2 + 2^2 + (-3)^2$$
$$+ (-1^2) + 1^2 + (-1^2) + 0^2 + 0^2$$
$$+ 0^2 + 1^2 + (-1^2)$$

$= 22$ **1**

$r_s = 1 - \dfrac{6 \times 22}{14(14^2 - 1)} = 0.952$ (correct to 3 d.p.)   **2**

H_0 : no association between prosperity and death rate; H_1 : positive association between prosperity and death rate.   **2**

Critical value is 0.4637 at 5% significance level.   **1**

∴ Reject H_0 and conclude there is a positive association between prosperity and death rate.   **1**

A one-tailed test is appropriate since we are looking for a positive association.

(ii) The comment is not justified since a correlation between two variables does not mean that a change in one causes a change in the other.   **2**

This is an important point.

(iii) Death rates in an area depend on the age of the population.   **1**

An area with a lot of old people would have a higher death rate, for example.   **1**

Try and illustrate your answer.

5 (i) $X \sim $ B(90, 0.045)   **1**

E(X) = np = $90 \times 0.045 = 4.05$ which is small so a Poisson approximation with mean and variance 4.05 is appropriate. i.e. $X \sim $ Po (4.05) approximately.   **1**

P($X = 4$) $= \dfrac{4.05^4 \, e^{-4.05}}{4!}$ **1**

$= \underline{0.195}$ (correct to 3 d.p.)   **1**

Note the hint of independence in the question.

Answer	Mark	Examiner's tip

(ii) The sample proportion would follow a

$N\left(p, \dfrac{pq}{n}\right)$ distribution approximately.   **1**

i.e. $N\left(0.045, \dfrac{0.045 \times 0.955}{400}\right)$ **1**

with $H_0 : p = 0.045 \quad H_1 : p > 0.045$ **1**   Since we are looking to see whether p is larger.

$$Z_{\text{test}} = \dfrac{\dfrac{25}{400} - 0.045}{\sqrt{\dfrac{0.045 \times 0.955}{400}}}$$

$= 1.688$ (correct to 3 d.p.)   **2**

The critical value for a one tailed test at the 5% level is 1.6449   The form of the alternative hypothesis requires a one-tailed test.

We therefore reject H_0 and conclude that there is <u>significant evidence to believe that 0.045 is an underestimate.</u>   **1**

6 (a) $\hat{\mu} = \dfrac{8460}{100} = \underline{84.6}$ **1**

(b) $s^2 = \dfrac{1}{99}\left(716\,400 - \dfrac{8460^2}{100}\right) = 6.9\dot{0}$ **1**

Standard error of $\hat{\mu}$ is $\dfrac{s}{\sqrt{n}} = \dfrac{\sqrt{6.9\dot{0}}}{10}$ **1**   Remember this answer is printed so show your working carefully.

$= \underline{0.263 \text{ approximately}}$ **1**

(c) $H_0 : \mu = 85 \quad H_1 : \mu < 85$

$Z_{\text{test}} = \dfrac{84.6 - 85}{0.263} = -1.521$ (correct to 3 d.p.)   **1**

The critical value at the 5% level is -1.6449 **1**   Note a one-tailed test is appropriate here since we are looking for a decrease.

$Z_{\text{test}} = -1.522 > -1.6449$ <u>so we accept H_0 and conclude that there is no evidence to suggest that the mean is lower than 85.</u>   **2**

(d) We would reject H_0 if $\dfrac{\hat{\mu} - 85}{0.263} < -1.6449$

i.e. $\bar{\mu} < 84.567$ **2**

The power of the test $= P(\text{reject } H_0 \mid \mu = 84)$

$= P\left(Z < \dfrac{84.576 - 84}{0.263}\right)$

$= P(Z < 2.156)$

$= 0.9838 + \dfrac{16}{20} \times (0.9846 - 0.9838)$

$= \underline{0.98 \text{ (correct to 2 d.p.)}}$ **2**

Answer	Mark	Examiner's tip

7 (i) $H_0 : p = 0.5$; $H_1 : p > 0.5$
since vicar believes a greater proportion of husbands are older than their wives.   **3**

(ii) Let X = number of couples with the husband older than the wife.
$P(X = 14) = {}^{19}C_{14} \, 0.5^{14} \, 0.5^5 = \underline{0.0222}$ **2**
$P(X \geq 14)$
$= ({}^{19}C_{14} + {}^{19}C_{15} + {}^{19}C_{16} + {}^{19}C_{17} + {}^{19}C_{18} + {}^{19}C_{19}) \, 0.5^{19}$ **1**
$= \underline{0.0318}$ **2**

(iii) $P(X \geq 14) < 0.05 \therefore$ reject H_0 and conclude a greater proportion of husbands are older than their wives.   **3**   State your conclusion clearly in the context of the original problem.

(iv) e.g. The sample is from a single part of country and involves one group of people (i.e. those who marry in church)
$\therefore$ conclusions extended to whole population are unlikely to be true.   **3**   Three marks for two objections and a statement as to the effect these have.

8 $\sum x = 156.943$ **1**
$\sum x^2 = 2052.980\,889$ **2**
$\bar{x} = \dfrac{156.943}{12} = 13.078\,583$ **2**

$s^2 = \dfrac{1}{11}\left(2052.980\,889 - \dfrac{156.943^2}{12}\right)$ An unbiased estimate for variance is needed here.
$= 0.035\,344\,083$ **2**

$H_0 : \mu = 13 \quad H_1 : \mu \neq 13$ **2**

$t_{\text{test}} = \dfrac{13.078\,58\dot{3} - 13}{\dfrac{\sqrt{0.035\,344\,083}}{\sqrt{12}}} = 1.448$ **2**   A t-distribution must be used because n is too small to use the Central Limit Theorem.

$\upsilon = 12 - 1 = 11$ **1**

At the 5% significance level with a two-tailed test the critical value needed is 2.201   **1**

$\underline{1.448 < 2.201 \text{ so we accept } H_0 \text{ and conclude}}$
$\underline{\text{that the production line is producing fuses which}}$
$\underline{\text{blow at 13 amps.}}$ **2**

9 CHI-SQUARED TESTS

Answer	Mark	Examiner's tip

1

Flight direction	0° – 90°	90° – 180°	180° – 270°	270° – 360°
Observed frequency	30	35	36	27
Expected frequency	32	32	32	32

1

H_0 : no preference for any direction i.e. uniform
    distribution is the correct model.

H_1 : there is a preference for a particular direction   **1**

$\upsilon = 4 - 1 = 3$ **1**   One restriction i.e. totals agree.

$$\chi^2_{calc} = \sum \frac{O^2}{E} - N = \frac{30^2}{32} + \frac{35^2}{32} + \frac{36^2}{32} + \frac{27^2}{32} - 128$$

$$= 1{\cdot}6875$$ **2**

Critical value at 5% level is $7{\cdot}815$ **1**

Since $\chi^2_{calc} < 7{\cdot}815$ we accept H_0 and conclude
<u>that there is no significant evidence to suggest
that the birds have preference for any direction
when released.</u>   **1**

2 (a) H_0 : Snoring and heart disease are not related

        H_1 : Snoring and heart disease are related   **1**

O/E	Never snores	Occasionally snores	Snores nearly every night	Snores every night	Total
Heart disease	24 / 61.1	35 / 28.3	21 / 9.4	30 / 11.2	110
No heart disease	1355 / 1317.9	603 / 609.7	192 / 203.6	224 / 242.8	2374
	1379	638	213	254	2484

Use $\dfrac{\text{row total} \times \text{column total}}{\text{grand total}}$
to calculate expected frequencies.

2

$\upsilon = (2 - 1) \times (4 - 1) = 3$ **1**

$\chi^2_{5\%}(3) = 7.815$ **1**

$$\chi^2_{calc} = \sum \frac{O^2}{E} - N$$

$$= \frac{24^2}{61.1} + \frac{35^2}{28.3} + \frac{21^2}{9.4} + \frac{30^2}{11.2} + \frac{1355^2}{1317.9}$$

$$+ \frac{603^2}{609.7} + \frac{192^2}{203.6} + \frac{224^2}{242.8} - 2484$$

Use the quicker computational
form for χ^2_{calc}.

$$= 73.2$$ **2**

<u>Since $73.2 > 7.815$ we reject H_0 and conclude
that snoring and heart disease are related.</u>   **1**   State the conclusion in context.

(b) Heart disease sufferers tend to snore more
than non-sufferers.   **1**

More snore every night or nearly every
night than expected.   **1**   Make sure you give a reason.

Answer	Mark	Examiner's tip

(c) The data show that there is a relationship but not a causal relationship. **1**

It could be that some other factor causes both snoring and heart disease. **1**   Make sure that you explain your answer, but *briefly*.

3 (i) $\bar{x} = \dfrac{6\times0+18\times1+\cdots+9\times5}{100} = 2.5$ **1**

x	0	1	2	3	4	5	6+	5+
O	6	18	30	21	16	9	0	9
E	8.21	20.52	25.65	21.38	13.36	6.68	4.20	10.88

combine

3   Notice the need to make the last class open-ended and to ensure that each expected frequency ≥ 5.

$\upsilon = 6 - 2 = 4$ **1**   The extra restriction is due to the calculated mean.

$\chi^2_{\text{calc}} = \dfrac{6^2}{8.21} + \dfrac{18^2}{20.52} + \ldots + \dfrac{9^2}{10.88} - 100 = 2.495$

H_0 : distribution is Poisson with mean 2.5 **1**

H_1 : distribution is not Poisson with mean 2.5 **1**

Critical value $\chi^2_{5\%}$ (4) = 9.488

$\therefore$ Since $\chi^2_{\text{calc}} < 9.488$ accept H_0 and conclude data has Poisson distribution with mean 2.5 **2**

(ii) $1.141 < 9.488$ so we accept that the data can be modelled by a Binomial distribution. **1**

(iii) Binomial has a lower χ^2_{calc} value so is a better fit. **1**

Binomial has improbable upper limit of 10. **1**

4

	Most fillings		
O/E	L	R	Total
LH	12 / 7.6	8 / 12.4	20
RH	7 / 11.4	23 / 18.6	30
Total	19	31	50

3 $n(\text{L} \cap \text{LH}) = \frac{19\times20}{50}$, etc using $\dfrac{\text{row total} \times \text{column total}}{\text{grand total}}$

$\upsilon = 1$ $\therefore$ use Yates' correction. **2**   Yates' correction must be used when $\upsilon = 1$.

$\chi^2_{\text{calc}} = \sum \dfrac{\left(|O - E| - 0.5\right)^2}{E}$

$= \dfrac{\left(|12 - 7.6| - 0.5\right)^2}{7.6} + \dfrac{\left(|8 - 12.4| - 0.5\right)^2}{12.4}$

$+ \dfrac{\left(|7 - 11.4| - 5.2\right)^2}{11.4} + \dfrac{\left(|23 - 18.6| - 0.5\right)^2}{18.6}$ **3**

$= \dfrac{3.9^2}{7.6} + \dfrac{3.9^2}{12.4} + \dfrac{3.9^2}{11.4} + \dfrac{3.9^2}{18.6}$ **1**

$= 5.380$ **1**

Answer	Mark	Examiner's tip

H_0 : Handedness and side of mouth with most fillings are independent. — **1**

H_1 : Handedness and side of mouth with most fillings are dependent. — **1**

The critical value $\chi^2_{5\%}(1) = 3.841$ — **1**

The calculated value is > critical value

$\therefore$ reject H_0 and conclude that which side most fillings occur on is related to whether a person is left- or right-handed. — **2**

5 (a)

Use $\dfrac{\text{row total} \times \text{column total}}{\text{grand total}}$ to get expected frequencies.

O/E	Emotion indicated				
Gender	Anger	Pain	Happiness	Love	Total
Female	$27/29.1$	$17/21.4$	$19/14.8$	$39/36.7$	102
Male	$34/31.9$	$28/23.6$	$12/16.2$	$38/40.3$	112
Total	61	45	31	77	214

2

H_0 : no relationship between gender and emotion associated with the colour red — **1**

H_1 : there is a relationship between gender and emotion associated with the colour red — **1**

$\upsilon = (2-1) \times (4-1) = 3$ — **1**

$$\chi^2_{\text{calc}} = \sum \frac{O^2}{E} - N$$

$$= \frac{27^2}{29.1} + \frac{17^2}{21.4} + \ldots + \frac{38^2}{40.3} - 214$$

$$= 4.571$$

2

The critical value at the 5% level is 7.815 — **1**

Since $\chi^2_{\text{calc}} < 7.815$ we therefore accept H_0 and conclude there is not significant evidence to believe there is a relationship between gender and the emotion associated with the colour red. — **2**

(b) $H_0 : p = 0.3$ $H_1 : p > 0.3$ — **1**

From sample $P_s = \frac{77}{214}$ so an estimate for the variance of the sample proportion is

Note that the claim is our alternative hypothesis

$$\frac{\frac{77}{214} \times \frac{137}{214}}{214} = 0.001\,076\,39$$ — **1**

$$Z_{\text{test}} = \frac{\frac{77}{214} - 0.3}{\sqrt{0.001\,076\,39}} = 1.823$$ — **1**

$P_s \sim N(0.3,\ 0.001\,076\,39)$ approximately.

The critical value at 5% is 1.6449 — **1**

A one-tailed test is appropriate here since we are looking for an increase.

Answer	Mark	Examiner's tip

Since $Z_{\text{test}} > 1.6449$ we reject H_0 and conclude that there is significant evidence to believe that more than 30% of all children associate LOVE with the colour red. **2**

6 (a) $\bar{x} = \dfrac{\sum fx}{\sum f}$

$= \dfrac{28\times0+73\times1+65\times2+\ldots+10\times5}{28+73+65+\ldots+10}$ **1**

$= \dfrac{500}{250} = 2$ **1**

Be careful to show your working when the answer is printed on the paper.

(b) Total frequency is 250.

x	0	1	2	3	4	≥ 5
O	28	73	65	49	25	10
E	33.8	67.7	67.7	45.1	22.6	13.1

4

Note that the last class must be ≥ 5 because of infinite nature of the Poisson distribution; expected frequencies are given to 1 d.p.

$\chi^2{}_{\text{calc}} = \sum \dfrac{O^2}{E} - N$

$= \dfrac{28^2}{33.8} + \dfrac{73^2}{67.7} + \ldots + \dfrac{10^2}{13.1} - 250$

$= 2.84$ **2**

$\upsilon = 6 - 2 = 4$ **1**

Note use of quicker alternative formula for $\chi^2{}_{\text{calc}}$ which can be used when $\upsilon \geq 2$.

Note the extra restriction since mean must equal the mean calculated from the data not just one given to you.

H_0 : distribution Poisson with mean 2
H_1 : distribution not Poisson mean 2 **1**
Critical value $\chi^2{}_4 (5\%) = 9.488$ **1**
$\chi^2{}_{\text{calc}} <$ the critical value **1**
∴ the result is not significant and so Poisson with mean 2 is a good fit. **1**

State your conclusion in terms of the original problem.

(c) $H_0 : \mu = 10$ $H_1 : \mu < 10$ (5 pages now) **4**
$P(X \leq 4) = 0.0293$ (tables) **1**
< 0.05 so result is significant. **1**
∴ there is evidence to suggest that the mean number of errors per page has improved. **2**

Use tables.

Conclusion must be stated in the context of the original problem.

10 ESTIMATION

Answer	Mark	Examiner's tip

1 $\bar{x} = \dfrac{124.31 + 125.14 + 124.23 + 125.41 + 125.76}{5}$

$= 124.97$ **1**

90% confidence limits are $124.97 \pm 1.6449 \times \dfrac{0.85}{\sqrt{5}}$ **2**

The required confidence interval is
(124.34, 125.60)   **2**

Remember that accuracy to
2 decimal places is required.

90% of the confidence intervals contain the
mean μ so 10% do not.   **1**

10% of 40 = 4 so the expected number of
intervals that do not contain μ is <u>4.</u>   **1**

This gets to the heart of what the
percentage confidence of a
confidence interval means.

2 (a) $E(T_1) = \frac{1}{2}\{E(X) + E(Y)\} = \frac{1}{2}(\mu - 1 + \mu + 1)$

$= \mu$

$\therefore T_1$ is an unbiased estimator for μ **1**

An unbiased estimator gives an
expected value of μ.

$E(T_2) = \frac{1}{3}\{2E(X) + E(Y)\}$

$= \frac{1}{3}\{2(\mu - 1) + \mu + 1\}$

$= \dfrac{3\mu - 1}{3}$

$\therefore T_2$ is a biased estimator for μ **1**

$E(T_3) = \frac{1}{3}\{2E(X) + E(Y) + 1\}$

$= \frac{1}{3}\{2(\mu - 1) + \mu + 1 + 1\} = \mu$

$\therefore T_3$ is an unbiased estimator for μ **1**

(b) $\text{Var}(T_1) = \frac{1}{4}\{\text{Var}(X) + \text{Var}(Y)\} = \frac{3}{4}\sigma^2$ **1**

Remember $\text{Var}(aX) = a^2\,\text{Var}(X)$,
etc.

$\text{Var}(T_2) = \frac{1}{9}\{4\text{Var}(X) + \text{Var}(Y)\} = \frac{6}{9}\sigma^2 = \frac{2}{3}\sigma^2$ **1**

$\text{Var}(T_3) = \frac{1}{9}\{4\,\text{Var}(X) + \text{Var}(Y)\} = \frac{6}{9}\sigma^2 = \frac{2}{3}\sigma^2$ **1**

Remember adding 1 doesn't
change the variance.

T_2, T_3 have the same variance.

(c) T_3 has the smallest variance and is unbiased.   **1**

A good estimator is unbiased and
has the smallest variance possible.

3 (a) Required proportion $= \dfrac{679}{4850} = \underline{0.14}$ **1**

(b) 99% confidence limits are

$\dfrac{679}{4850} \pm 2.5758 \sqrt{\dfrac{\dfrac{679}{4850} \times \dfrac{4171}{4850}}{4850}}$ **2**

The confidence interval is <u>(0.127, 0.153)</u>   **2**

Answer	Mark	Examiner's tip

(c) The assumption is that the proportion of dissatisfied customers in the returned questionnaires is the same as the proportion of dissatisfied customers for all its customers. — **1**

Those returning the questionnaires are likely to have strong enough opinions to encourage them to return the questionnaire. $\therefore$ they are likely to provide an overestimate of dissatisfaction. — **1**

4 $\bar{x} = \dfrac{414 + 450}{2} = 432$ — **2, 1** — $\bar{x}$ is in the middle of the confidence interval.

$1.96\dfrac{\sigma}{\sqrt{85}} = \frac{1}{2}(450 - 414)$ — **4** — The right-hand side is half the width of the confidence interval.

$\sigma = 84.67$ — **1**

5 (a) $\bar{x} = \dfrac{6771}{20} = 338.55$ — **1**

$\bar{y} = \dfrac{3368}{10} = 336.8$ — **1**

(b) Confidence limits are

$(338.55 - 336.8) \pm 1.96 \sqrt{\dfrac{6.5^2}{20} + \dfrac{4.8^2}{10}}$ — **2** — Note the form of the variance for the combined data.

The confidence interval is $(-2.369, 5.869)$ — **2**

(c) Since 0 lies in the confidence interval and this corresponds to the means being the same this belief need not be amended. — **2** — This is quite a common request in a question.

6 (i) (a) $\hat{\mu} = \dfrac{2092.0}{200} = 10.46$ — **1**

(b) $\hat{\sigma}^2 = \dfrac{1}{199}\left(24994.5 - \dfrac{(2092.0)^2}{200}\right)$ — **1** — An unbiased estimate is needed here.

$= 15.64$ — **1**

One whose average (or expected) value is the population parameter it is being used to estimate. — **1** — This is a key definition.

(ii) $H_0 : \mu = 10 \quad H_1 : \mu > 10$

The critical z-value is $\dfrac{10.65 - 10}{\dfrac{\hat{\sigma}}{\sqrt{200}}} = \dfrac{10.65 - 10}{\dfrac{\sqrt{15.64}}{\sqrt{200}}}$ — **1** — Be careful to get the standard deviation right.

$= 2.324$ — **1**

$P(Z > 2.324) = 1 - P(Z < 2.324)$

$= 1 - \{0.9898 + \frac{4}{20}(0.9904 - 0.9898)\}$ — **1** — The significance level is the probability of exceeding the critical value.

$= 0.01008$ — **1**

This corresponds to a 1% significance level. — **1**

Answer	Mark	Examiner's tip

(iii) The central limit theorem applies since $n = 200$ for the sample. **1**

7 (i) Actual mean $= \dfrac{20 \times 59.4 - 96 + 69}{20} = \dfrac{1161}{20}$ **3**   Work out the correct total and divide by 20 using $\sum x = n\bar{x}$.

$= 58.05$ **1**

Actual variance $= \dfrac{\sum x^2}{n} - \bar{x}^2$

$= \dfrac{20\left(196.74 + 59.4^2\right) - 96^2 + 69^2}{20} - 58.05^2$ **3**   Work out the correct sum of squares using old $\sum x^2 = n(\text{old } \sigma^2 + \text{old } \bar{x}^2)$

$= \dfrac{70047}{20} - 58.05^2$ **1**

$= \underline{132.5475}$ **1**

(ii) $\hat{\mu} = \bar{x} = \underline{58.05}$ **1**   Using

$\hat{\sigma}^2 = \dfrac{n}{n-1} \times (\text{sample variance})$

where sample variance

$\hat{\sigma}^2 = \frac{20}{19} \times \text{sample variance} = \frac{20}{19} \times 132.5475$

$= \underline{139.524}$ **2** $= \dfrac{\sum x^2}{n} - \bar{x}^2$ is sometimes useful.

8 (i)

2   For unimodal positively skewed distributions the order is mode, median, mean.

(ii) $\bar{r} = \dfrac{35.5}{50} = 0.71$ **1**

$s^2 = \dfrac{1}{49}\left(33.2 - \dfrac{35.5^2}{50}\right) = 0.1632$ **1**   We need an unbiased estimate for the population variance here.

90% confidence limits are

$0.71 \pm 1.6449 \times \dfrac{\sqrt{0.1632}}{\sqrt{50}}$ **1**   Don't forget that $\dfrac{s}{\sqrt{n}}$ is the estimated standard deviation.

i.e. the required confidence interval is

$\underline{(0.616, 0.804)}$ **1**

The assumption is that the values of R are independent. **1**

(iii) We require $1.645 \dfrac{\sqrt{0.1632}}{\sqrt{n}} = 0.05$ **1**   Half the width is to be 0.05.

$n = 176.64$ i.e. $\underline{177 \text{ throws are required.}}$ **2**

Answer	Mark	Examiner's tip
The Central Limit Theorem has been used so Normality is only approximate.	1	
(iv) This is only a small sample from a non-Normal distribution.	1	
The Central Limit Theorem cannot be used as n is not large.	1	
The t-distribution cannot be used because the distribution is not normal.	1	Give reasons to explain your answers.

9 (a) $\bar{x} = \dfrac{34.7 + 34.4 + 35.1 + 34.6}{4} = 34.7$ — 1

95% confidence limits are $34.7 \pm 1.96 \times \dfrac{0.36}{\sqrt{4}}$ — 2 — Don't forget that the standard error of the mean is $\dfrac{\sigma}{\sqrt{n}}$.

Confidence interval is (34.3472, 35.0528) — 2

(b) Width $= 2 \times 1.96 \times \dfrac{0.36}{\sqrt{4}} = 0.7056$ — 1

(c) $2 \times z \times \dfrac{0.36}{\sqrt{4}} = 0.3 \Rightarrow z = 0.833$ — 2 — Notice the parallel with part (b).

$P(Z < 0.833) = 0.7967 + \tfrac{3}{10}(0.7995 - 0.7967)$

$= 0.79754$ — 1

We require $\{1 - 2(1 - P(Z \le 0.833))\} \times 100$

i.e. 59.5% confidence — 1 — Take the area in the two tails away from 1 and multiply the answer by 100.

(d) $2 \times 1.96 \times \dfrac{0.36}{\sqrt{n}} = 0.3$ — 2 — This time we are changing n.

$\sqrt{n} = 4.704 \Rightarrow n = 22.1$ — 1

To make the width as near to 0.3 kg as possible we require 22 weighings of the sack. — 1 — Notice that if the question had asked for a width of 0.3 kg or less we would have needed 23 weighings.